Cover design by Ahmed Raza
Interior design by Olivier Darbonville
Artwork by Lynn Tong

Library of Congress Cataloging-in-Publication Data: 2020907315

ISBN 978-1-7347754-2-6 (paperback)
ISBN 978-1-7347754-1-9 (e-book)

Printed in the United States of America.

The
WELL
SPOUSE

MY JOURNEY OF LOVE, RESILIENCE, AND ALZHEIMER'S

JoAnn Wingfield

A "formal night" while cruising in *Queen Mary 2*, August 2005.

In memory of

Clyde Wingfield, Charles Beebe, and Ronald Parks.

For caregivers everywhere.

———————

CONTENTS

ACKNOWLEDGMENTS

IT HAD ALWAYS BEEN MY DESIRE TO TELL MY STORIES as a spousal caregiver during my years taking care of my husband, when things were difficult, when I was solaced by friends and family or rescued by a stranger, or when I had those aha moments. It took several years of wondering and procrastinating for me to finally muster enough confidence to convince myself that my stories are worth telling, and that writing in a language that is not my native tongue is possible.

I give my gratitude to those who helped me through those challenging years of caregiving: you are the fabric of my stories; and to those who have reviewed, critiqued, and edited my manuscript: you are the catalyst for me to move these stories from being one person's memory to now having filled these pages for many to savor.

To my editors:

Dr. Claudia Eisen-Murphy, thank you for enduring my Chinglish-filled first draft, and for helping me make the transition from Chinglish to English. Your ability to make every criticism sound like music to my ears was amazing.

Dr. Catherine Barnhart, thank you for methodically helping me weave together the cultures of the East and the West, creating beauty from dreadfulness and harmony from chaos; and thank you for your exquisite translation from Chinese to English of the poems and quotations used in this book.

Christina Roth, thank you for meticulously reviewing and correcting the editorial aspects of my manuscript; for helping me uphold the structural, syntactical, and ideological integrity of the book.

Scott James, thank you for navigating me through the maze of publication in the digital age with your expertise, patience, and wisdom (are you too young for this compliment?); and for the beautiful website through which I can reach readers near and far.

To my family and friends:

Yun Lan, my sister in Shanghai, China, for tirelessly listening to my stories and always believing in my abilities to write them, sometimes more than I did. One day there will be a Chinese version, and you will be able to read it.

Lan Chen, my sister-in-law, for painstakingly reading my English manuscript, often with the help of a dictionary, and giving me candid feedback.

Joy Halpern, William Wingfield, Loren Wingfield, and Stuart Su, thank you for being my champions on the care journey, for filling in the gaps of my stories, and for being my family.

Dr. Gary Evans and Dr. Ellen Jackofsky, thank you for sharing my ups and downs. This is your story too.

Fan Lanyin, my friend since our Inner Mongolia years during the Cultural Revolution and an avid reader, thank you for your encouragement.

John Shao, Jonathan Everette, Susan Bloch, and Tom Prejean, all avid readers, your compliments are reassuring, and your critiques are inspiring. Thank you.

Julie Zhou, Mark Strong, Barbara LaSalle, "Punkin" and Debrah Javelet, Laurie Towe . . . while I could not possibly mention every person who has helped in shaping my stories, my appreciation is with all of you.

PROLOGUE

THIS BOOK TELLS THE STORY OF AN ORDINARY COUPLE on an ordinary path that has been described in the famous beginning phrase of Tolstoy's *Anna Karenina*, "All happy families are alike." On one ordinary day, one of them was diagnosed with Alzheimer's disease. Tests and trials followed. Would that particular kind of human relationship, universally known as love, endure? And if so, how?

Alzheimer's disease! To most people, the diagnosis is a grim matter. It is a death sentence, the worst kind, because it is a proclamation of a slow and agonizing death that usually lasts for years, sometimes over a decade. The diagnosis is a curse that takes with it many victims in addition to the one who is ill: family members and close friends are forced to witness the painful deterioration of the afflicted, and increasingly they have to step in to compensate for the lost abilities of their loved one.

In 2017, close to 50 million people worldwide were living with Alzheimer's disease, and this number is predicted to double every twenty years, reaching 75 million in 2030 and 131.5 million in 2050.[1] According to the Alzheimer's Association's 2019 annual report, approximately 5.8 million people in the United States are living with Alzheimer's disease. It is the sixth leading cause of death in the United States, and the fifth leading cause of death for those age sixty-five and older. Between 2000 and 2017, death certificates recorded an astonishing 145 percent increase in the number of deaths from Alzheimer's disease, while the number of deaths decreased from other major causes of death, e.g., prostate cancer, by 1.9 percent; heart disease, the number one cause of death, by 8.9 percent; stroke, by 12.7 percent; and HIV, by 60.6 percent.[2]

The report also noted that in 2018 alone, more than 16.1 million family members and other unpaid caregivers provided an estimated 18.5 billion hours of unpaid care that was valued close to a staggering $234 billion. Caregivers experience higher levels of burden, impaired mood, depression, and diminished health than people who aren't caregivers for those with dementia, and 38 percent of the caregivers, including spouses, partners, and family members, believe that caring for their loved one is their obligation. Often, the well spouse is the most affected. Emotionally, losing a spouse is losing one's most intimate relationship, one's "other half." Spousal caregivers are more likely than married noncaregivers to have physiological changes that may reflect declining physical health, including high levels of stress hormones, impaired immune function, slow wound healing, coronary heart disease, impaired function of the endothelium (the inner lining of blood vessels), and increased incidence of hypertension. Some of these changes may be associated with an increased risk of cardiovascular disease.[3]

It is a gloomy picture. So what does a person do to survive as a well spouse?

Through the twists and turns of my story of love and loss, sorrow and despair, misfortunes and calamities, secrets and betrayals, and friendship and compassion, I invite you into my world of caregiving. I wrote about my experience retrospectively and candidly, not to tell you that there is nobility in caregiving—although I believe there is—but that the nobility alone does not come close to outweighing the years of mundane tasks and endless drudgery caregiving entails. Being noble was never my purpose, because I did not set out to be a caregiver. I had to rise to the task. When I started this journey, facing so many uphill battles and uncertainties, I wondered if I would find enough strength to go through it, and how. I wished I knew what was to come so I could be prepared. And I wished for a light in the darkness, however dim and distant, to point me the way, to show me the end, and to give me hope. Now as the one who has left the troubled waters behind and remains standing, I offer my stories to other well spouses, family caregivers, and those who care. When you are experiencing sorrow, fear, frustration, agony, exhaustion, and depression, and when the level of stress makes you feel on the verge of a total breakdown, know that you are not alone. There is not *the* way, there is not a single *right* way, and there is definitely not an *easy* way, but there are paths through this arduous terrain. Many of us have found a way, and some ways are better than others. I found mine, and I wish you success in finding yours.

This is not a how-to book—there is an abundance of those; nor a book on the pathology and science of Alzheimer's disease—again, they are not in short supply; nor a book about the Alzheimer's patient, the ill spouse—there is an abundance of those, too. Instead, this is a book about the well spouse, the one who takes care of business. It is about her loss, despair, and struggles, as well as her love, kindness, courage, compassion, and friendships. I am offering this book to console and confer, to inspire, and to instill hope in the hearts of those who, as well spouses and family caregivers, are struggling through one of the direst human conditions: caring for an Alzheimer's patient.

Although my well-spouse journey unfolded over the course of nine years, this story is not told as a straightforward chronology of my husband's mental and physical deterioration. Instead, structured loosely along the chronological line, I have narrated the stories through a series of vignettes in which I, the well spouse, learn to cope with the unknown; to overcome the fear; to fight and accept; to find strength from past experiences; to mend my safety net torn by a dreadful disease with the support of people surrounding me; to be able to love and laugh while grieving; to grow, emotionally and spiritually; and finally, to mourn, to remember, and to renew.

Charlie Chaplin said, "To truly laugh, you must be able to take your pain, and play with it." As you read on, soon you will encounter plenty of sad stories. But I hope that, occasionally, you will also feel amused and charmed by a life that was laden with pain, loss, and grief.

These might be your stories now, or one day, or they may be the stories of a friend or loved one of yours. Before you venture on, I want to tell you a true story that I heard from a friend years ago:

> One night several patients were in a hospital observation room. A wife was with her eighty-something husband, Oliver, who had Alzheimer's disease but was there for some other problems. As the wife pulled the curtain around Oliver's bed to help him to bed, Oliver whispered to her, "Hon, I got to pee." So the wife handed him a urinal and turned away to pull down the sheet and blanket. Then she felt a warm stream of liquid on her leg. She turned and looked. There was Oliver, holding the urinal in his left hand nowhere near his peeing "thing," which he held in his right hand. She quickly grabbed the urinal from him. As she was guiding Oliver, she screamed, "Oliver! Baby! You are eighty years old, and you don't know how to use it yet. Put it in! PUT IT IN!"
>
> From the other side of the curtain, howling laughter burst out, and the wife realized what she had just said. They all laughed until they cried.

Being able to laugh is perhaps one of the most unique human traits. We must learn to laugh even when life makes us cry.

Clyde and the author in their home on Ranchita Drive in Dallas,
Texas, shortly after Clyde's diagnosis.

One

THE DIAGNOSIS

*In the middle of the journey of our life I came to myself
within a dark wood where the straight way was lost.*

—DANTE ALIGHIERI, The Divine Comedy

FATE LIKES TO DEAL US UNEXPECTED CARDS. In a split moment, one's life can take drastic turns. Sometimes, it is not for the better, and often, we are not prepared. Yet, people must choose to play the cards the best they know how.

It was an ordinary day in October 2002. As my plane was descending into Boston's Logan Airport, I took in the view from my window: fall had already painted one of those spectacular landscapes so characteristic of New England—fiery red, simmering crimson, glittering gold, and various shades of yellow spread across the fields. When I had left Dallas a few hours earlier, summer still had its distinctive presence.

Dragging my ultralight carry-on through the chaos of Logan's crowded hallways, I walked briskly to catch a taxi before a line formed. The vigorous walking made me hot. Occasionally, a breeze came in through the automatic doors with a suggestion of the cool, crisp day outside, where I could see the Boston sun shining happily over a tapestry of color. Carefully avoiding collisions with other travelers in their comings and goings, I was vaguely conscious of the loudspeakers' monophonic tone warning travelers to be vigilant of unattended luggage and suspicious behavior, somehow managing to diminish people's awareness with each repetition.

My cell phone rang. I immediately recognized that the call was from the Miami area, but the number was new to me. Without slowing down, I responded with the usual matter-of-fact tone I used for calls of unknown origin, "This is JoAnn."

At the other end was an unfamiliar male voice with a heavy foreign accent. *Russian, Polish, or was it Romanian?*

"I am Dr. Rabinowitz, an ophthalmology neurologist at the University of Miami medical center. Do you have a moment? I need to talk to a family member about Dr. Wingfield's diagnosis. He said I should talk to you, no one else."

My heart dropped. Suddenly, I broke into a cold sweat and felt weak.

"Yes," I replied, holding my breath as if the man at the other end of the line might evaporate into thin air if I breathed too hard. All the chaos and noise around me had receded, as though I were all alone in a vast, empty hall. I managed to sit down on a nearby bench and continued, "I have been expecting your call."

The day before, in Dallas, Clyde had called me from Miami, where he had been undergoing psychological and cognitive assessments. "My psychological evaluation is complete. The doctor said that I have dementia."

"Dementia? What is dementia?" A quick search of the English dictionary in my brain did not yield any meaning. *Another new English word for me?* It sounded quite innocent, like "differentia," *small deviations*, nothing to cause alarm.

"Dementia is a kind of memory loss. I guess I've just gotten lazy since I retired." Clyde didn't seem to be alarmed either.

"Did the doctor say what the cause was? What should you do? What should I do? What should *we* do?" I was always eager to attack a problem.

"The doctor said it could be Alzheimer's disease. I told him *do not* label me with anything. I don't want to be put into a box!"

So typical of men! So typical of Clyde! Self-assured, he would never in a million years let anyone tell him who he was, what to do, or what problem he had, not even his doctor. Instead, most unambiguously, he told the doctor exactly what to say.

Born in the early 1930s in a small Southern town, Clyde was a Depression-era baby. When he was about four years old, he contracted pneumonia and nearly died. He remembered lying in bed, unable to move or talk, listening to the doctor telling his mother that he would be dead before sunrise and hearing his aunt asking his father to remove his baby shoes from the bedside because, when he was dead, his mother would never remove them. Miraculously, he beat the doctor's prediction and survived. At the tender age of twenty-two, after graduating from university and finishing his ROTC training, Clyde became an Air Force officer. It was then the end of the Korean War. He flew airplanes and presented intelligence briefings to generals. After the war, on GI Bill funding, he completed a master's degree in finance and a PhD in public administration, then went on to serve in senior positions in higher education, including several university presidencies.

He was well read and well traveled, quick to give and reluctant to receive, easy to amuse but difficult to fool; he could be frugal but was never stingy, and thrifty but never cheap. He feared nothing and stopped at no obstacles. He used to quote to me in his magnificent baritone voice from the King James Bible with an Air Force twist and an exaggerated seriousness, "Yea, though I walk through the valley of the shadow of death, I will fear no evil: for I am the meanest SOB of all!"

Nothing called "dementia" could possibly defeat a man like Clyde.

But Alzheimer's is an entirely different beast. Didn't President Reagan have that?

When I heard the term *Alzheimer's disease*, the word *dementia* lost its ring of innocence. Still, I held on to the "Wingfield Confidence"—Wingfield may be wrong, but never in doubt. Surely there could be a mistake. Surely there would be something we could do. Hadn't Clyde always provided more solutions to every problem we had ever encountered?

Clyde's voice pulled me back from my thoughts. "Dr. Rabinowitz said he needed to talk to family members about the diagnosis. I told him the only one he has my permission to talk to is you. He will call you soon."

We agreed that the doctor's name would be *Rabbit*, because it was too hard for me to pronounce, much less to remember how to spell, such a complicated name.

"OK. I can hardly wait for you to be back." I ended that conversation.

I spent the rest of the day trying to convince myself there was nothing to be worried about. Hadn't Clyde said there was nothing to be worried about? Wasn't he *almost* always right? Yet an uneasy feeling lingered. That word, *Alzheimer's . . .*

"Are you aware of the psychological and cognitive evaluations we were working on with Dr. Wingfield last week?" On the other end of the line continued Rabbit's Eastern European–infused voice.

"Yes."

"I have completed the analysis. Dr. Wingfield has dementia."

"Clyde told me that. He said that dementia is a form of memory loss. It is quite common as people age. What can you tell me about his dementia?"

"Well, dementia is a general term for memory loss. There are many forms of dementia. My diagnosis of Dr. Wingfield is that he has Alzheimer's disease, a specific form of dementia. It is a progressive and degenerative cognitive disease that is *not reversible*."

All of a sudden, the air at the airport felt thinner, and I thought I couldn't breathe. *Did he say what I thought he said? Did he mean what he said? Did I hear what he said? Did I understand correctly what was said?* After all, my English comprehension had failed me many times before. Small misunderstandings sometimes caused big misunderstandings, like *pleasure* and *pressure*, *ego* and *eagle*, *vacation* and *vocation*, or *message* and *massage*. One time I emailed a male colleague telling him that I would give him a *massage*, whereas I really meant *message*. It puzzled me why he looked so awkward when I saw him later.

But Rabbit was clear. So clear that the words Alzheimer's disease, though coming remotely from over a thousand miles away, were brutally distinct, striking me like the blows of a heavyweight boxer and making me dizzy.

"Dr. Wingfield has made it very clear to me that I should not label him. I will respect his wishes by not calling him an Alzheimer's patient, but I must talk to a family member about his disease. He said the only one I should talk to is you."

"Yes. He told me that."

"Dr. Wingfield said that he is retired and is now a consultant to the University of Miami Board of Trustees. Is that true?"

"Yes."

"Dr. Wingfield cannot make decisions. As his physician, I must tell you that it is inconceivable to me that he still works." Dr. Rabbit sounded appalled that a consultant to the board of his university was mentally impaired. "His cognitive ability is severely compromised. He does not have the faculties to make sound judgments."

How ironic! Didn't Clyde used to repeat the old joke, "Old university presidents never die. They just lose their faculties"?

"He said that he still travels by himself. Is this true?"

"Yes. We sometimes travel together, but he frequently travels to Miami by himself for his work with the board. I can't always be with him on these trips, since I work at Southern Methodist University, in Dallas." I felt a need to explain, as if I were guilty of not always being at his side. "The rest of the time, he stays in Dallas with me."

"Dr. Wingfield cannot travel alone. His memory is impaired. He will get confused and he will get lost. It is not safe for him to travel alone. He must be with someone when he travels. His condition will deteriorate. He will eventually lose not only all his ability to remember, comprehend, and recognize but also his ability to take care of himself. You will need to safe-proof your home as everything can be hazardous to him, and as his condition worsens, he cannot be left alone without help."

At the other end of the line, Rabbit's voice continued to tell me candidly, though not inconsiderably, about the dismal prospects of Alzheimer's disease. Meanwhile, my mind took off on its own path. For a couple of years, I had suspected that something was not right with Clyde's mind. Certain things had started to go peculiarly wrong: occasionally, he would leave drawers open, leave the water running, fail to turn off lights, and even sometimes forget to flush toilets. And he began to have traffic accidents. This sloppiness was most definitely un-Clyde, who had always been clean, neat, and an excellent driver. I thought that his good behavior was due to his Air Force training and from having worked and lived in Manhattan and other big cities where driving skill was more essential to one's survival, but he attributed his remarkable self-discipline to having had a good mother. To try to make sense of his seemingly careless behaviors, I had even joked with him that he might have Alzheimer's disease.

To try to resolve my lingering suspicion over "Does he have it or does he not have it?", I had started to educate myself about Alzheimer's disease. While I had not been able to diagnose him myself, I had some general understanding of what was in store for a person with Alzheimer's and for me, his well spouse.

I knew Clyde would gradually descend into a black hole, where there would be no friends left, and there would be no family left; everything would become unrecognizable, then everything would become incomprehensible. The past would disappear, and the future would never come. Eventually, there would be nothing left in his consciousness, neither him nor me. Yet our lives would continue. For years? For decades?

On the other end of the phone, Dr. Rabbit ended the conversation with these sympathetic words: "I am very sorry. Your life will be very difficult as his disease progresses. Take care, and good luck to you."

Trickles of warm, salty liquid in my mouth made me realize that I was weeping, in public. Pain of losing a loved one is a pain so intense that no painkiller, regardless how powerful, can ease. I had just been given a death sentence for Clyde, the man who for the past thirteen years had been my mentor, my anchor, my partner, my best friend, and my protector. I was facing the most profound loss of my life. In the vast, crowded hallways of Logan Airport, I felt terribly alone as I sensed that Clyde's strong support, the support that had sustained me like indestructible pillars, was crumbling. Sadness crushed on me like a tumbled mountain, and the ground underneath me fissured. At the same time, from the deepest core of my being, a somber determination slowly emerged: *Clyde, you have made me a stronger woman. I can and will take this journey with you to wherever the end might be.*

"The will to win, the desire to succeed" were the words of the ancient Chinese philosopher Confucius, the wisdom of my ancestors.[4]

With these words of encouragement by my ancestors echoing in my mind, I walked out of the airport, Dr. Rabbit's parting words still resonating:

"... good luck to you."

"An Uphill Battle." Whistler Mountain, British Columbia, Canada.

Front yard view of the Ranchita home.

Backyard view of the Ranchita home.

Two

HOME SWEET HOME

If you go anywhere, even paradise, you will miss your home.

—MALALA YOUSAFZAI,
the youngest Nobel Peace Prize recipient

IN 2003, THE HUMAN GENOME PROJECT, conducted by scientists around the globe, was declared complete. The project involved sequencing and mapping the DNA base pairs found in the human genome, identifying a broader array of human subjects for further sequencing, and investigating new applications for the study. It was expected to bring enormous long-term benefits to the fields of science and medicine. Among them is our increased ability to understand, diagnose, and develop treatments for diseases like Alzheimer's that have been considered irreversible and terminal. The distant hope for an Alzheimer's cure came a little closer.

For Clyde and me, it was the beginning of the long journey of learning to live with Alzheimer's disease. Before Thanksgiving 2002, in response to Dr. Rabbit's unambiguous assessment of Clyde's cognitive condition, Clyde gave up his work as a consultant to the University of Miami Board of Trustees (long overdue), extricated himself from his dwelling in Key Biscayne in sunny Florida, and moved to Dallas in the Lone Star State to live with me.

Texas, a whole different country! Everything in Texas is big: Women favor massive hairstyles, oversized jewelry, and what I thought of as exaggerated makeup. Men wear hats the size of umbrellas and belt buckles as big as dinner plates. Jellybeans are the size of goose eggs, and everyone drives a pickup truck. Why?

"To haul ass!" So I was told.

Big D is Dallas, as the Big Apple is New York: fashionable, cosmopolitan, and B-I-G. In the far north panhandle of Big D, on a corner lot on a street named Ranchita, a "little ranch," stood a sprawling one-story house. The silver-gray roof was newly installed. I had picked out the light color to bounce off some of the ferocious Texas summer sun. The brick walls combined uneven pale red, worn white, and heathery gray, giving it a somewhat raggedy texture. Savannah Gray, perhaps? The color of the house's exterior reminded me of the color of a Caucasian face, Clyde's, in particular: fair, pinkish skin under salt-and-pepper hair. Both aged well, I told Clyde. In spring, the circular driveway in front of the house wrapped around a flowerbed in which two tall pear-less pear trees produced a profusion of white flowers. Tulips and daffodils, red, white, yellow, sprouted randomly, attracting the attention of passersby: people, dogs, squirrels, ducks, birds, butterflies. All summer and into the fall, the glittering blue water of the pool in the backyard tempted everyone into the water, even without the call of bewitching mermaids; crimson crape myrtles swayed their limbs by the side of the pool, dropping wilted red flowers into the blue water, forcing the pool guy and me to chase out the debris continuously. None of us complained, as everyone, every being, must understand that one of the requirements in life is the perpetual adjustment to changes.

This was an ordinary Texas house in an ordinary middle-class Dallas neighborhood: it was big. The house had four spacious bedrooms, two vast living rooms, and multiple essential and nonessential peripheral rooms. In the backyard, the pool made the Texas summer a little more bearable. But my real reason for having a pool was so that my son, Stuart, who had just started college at Southern Methodist University, would come home more often. I pictured young people, boys and girls, splashing around the pool,

At Stuart's high
school graduation.

filling the backyard with laughter. Wishful thinking, as it turned out. The
coed life on campus was far more exciting to an almost-twenty-something
than swimming under his parents' *potentially* watchful eyes.

Even without Stuey and his energetic pals, the house was definitely
a lovely home for Clyde and me. We nourished our minds and bodies
with simple food over intricate conversations, at least for the first couple
of years; we shared scrumptious feasts with family and friends; and ah,
how the aroma of coffee and toast permeated the house every morning!
Summer evenings, Clyde and I waited for the sun to go down to have a
race in the pool.

Sometime during the first year, Mom and Dad came to visit from
Shanghai. Dad and Clyde chatted for hours on the patio, about China, the
US, and the world in between; and about history, politics, and everything
beyond. Dad spoke about two dozen English words and Clyde was losing
his English words, making them more or less equal in English conversation.

Clyde and the
author's dad,
Westmont, Illinois,
2003.

Winter came. With the blaze in the fireplace radiating warmth, Clyde and I danced in the ballroom-sized living room to the music of the Big Band Era. The sound of my daily rudimentary piano practicing accompanied Clyde's resonant baritone:

"Nobody knows the trouble I've seen, nobody knows my sorrow . . ."

"A house is no home unless it contains food and fire for the mind as well as for the body," said Margaret Fuller, echoing Benjamin Franklin.

As the seasons passed, it became more evident that Clyde's faculties were leaving him. No one could see it because the positive identification of Alzheimer's disease can only be made postmortem; yet, unmistakably, I felt it, and, irrevocably, I knew.

Summer days in Big D were sunny, humid, and long. On one such day, I was in the kitchen doing whatever. From time to time I looked out at the backyard, taking pleasure in the red blossoms floating on the surface of the blue water, and the water glittering in response to occasional breezes; birds whose names we didn't know dipping into the water and chasing each other up to the sky again. And then I became aware that Clyde was walking, from one room to another, silently, dreamingly; peering through each room, silently, dreamingly. His eyes were open wide, inquisitive, bewildered, the eyes of a little child seeing something new for the first time, yet there was no excitement, only bafflement and apprehension.

"Baby, are you looking for something?" I asked.

No reply.

"Maybe I can help?" Hearing no response, I put down the *whatever* I was doing, went to him, held his hand in mine, and started to walk with him, from one room to the next. Somehow, the vast living room appeared bigger and emptier.

"Honey, where are we? I don't know where I am," he said, like a child, a lost child.

"Baby, you are home. This is our home."

"Really? I don't recognize anything."

"Baby, look, here are your books. That is your chair. Remember now?"

He made an effort to remember but came up with nothing.

"Come, let me show you your clothes and shoes." Without letting go of his hand, I took him to the bedroom. The T-shirt he had worn the night before was lying on a chaise. I picked it up, sniffed it, and held it to his nose. "Smell it. Can you tell that it is full of your DNA?"

He sniffed, docilely obeying my instructions like a well-behaved child, and then looked at me. His eyes told me that he was still at a loss. Later I learned that a diminished sense of smell is one of the symptoms of Alzheimer's disease.

"Look at this picture. Who are these people?" I picked up a photo on his dresser.

"I don't know these people." He studied the picture for a while, his greenish-gray eyes, once alive with intelligence, now dim. In the years to come, those eyes would become completely hollow.

In the picture, taken in this very house around Christmastime less than a year before, were Clyde's brother, sister-in-law, sister, son, and daughter-in-law. His daughter and her family had not been able to come that year. We were all in a festive mood in front of a lit Christmas tree. Everyone looked beautiful; everyone seemed happy. I had not yet broken the news of Clyde's Alzheimer's to any of the family members. He had been very firm on that point: "I don't want you to tell anyone about my diagnosis."

"Do you recognize these kids?" Seeing his struggle, I moved on to another photo. "They are your offspring. See, here you are holding your

Clyde holding his grandson.

granddaughter when she was still a toddler. Look at those dimples on her chubby legs. Look at how proudly you were smiling." He had been carrying a smaller version of this picture in his wallet for many years. The first time he showed it to me during one of our early dates, I was shocked. *How was it possible for this dark-haired man to have such blond offspring?* He explained that his daughter and her children lived in Florida, where the sun had bleached their hair. Most Chinese people have dark hair. Except for aging, the hair color never varies, regardless of weather or season, regardless of generation.

Posing as an old-time couple.

To jog his memory, I picked up another photo. "You must know these two good-looking people." In this picture, intentionally yellowed and faded to look vintage, appeared a man and a woman dressed as a pioneer and an American Indian from the era of the Oregon Trail, standing next to an antique traveling trunk. "Do you remember that I had to twist your arm to get you to take this picture with me when we were in Sam's Club?" I used to tell Clyde that on our "little ranch" lived a cowboy—him—and an Indian woman—me. With my dark eyes, dark hair, and relatively dark complexion, I could easily pass as an American Indian.

"How about this one?" Old colonial buildings along the Bund in Shanghai stood behind a dark-haired, bright-eyed couple, looking youthful and happy. That picture was taken in 1997 on our first trip to China together, before all the skyscrapers mushroomed and dominated the skylines of the Bund.

In the Bund, Shanghai, 1997.

"Baby, this is you and me on our first trip to Shanghai together. Look at how dark your hair was."

Happy days those were! "Gone are the days when my heart was young and gay," Old Black Joe chimed in as I held the photos.[5] Suddenly and unexpectedly, a sense of loss filled me like flooding water: *Gone are the days!*

Resolutely and decisively, I rejected the dark force that was trying to engulf me, to suffocate me with sadness, pain, and grief. A well spouse was a protector, strong and steady. I was the well spouse!

"Come over here. Come and sit with me." I quickly moved us from the scene so I wouldn't be swept away by my abrupt melancholy.

Hand in hand across the rooms, we went into the kitchen. I made a pot of tea for both of us. While the warm liquid eased away my grief, and while I continued doing *whatever* I had been doing, perhaps preparing an excellent-looking piece of fish (beauty is in the eye of the beholder) or cleaning vegetables, I took comfort in the fact that I still had my husband. I began a simple conversation. Getting Clyde to reminisce about the past was one of the ways to help him keep the old memories longer. Familiar subjects made him less confused and more relaxed.

"Clyde, where were you born?"

"How old were you when your sister was born?"

"Were you ever hungry as a child?"

But after a while, he grew restless again. Without a word, he stood up and started pacing again, quietly, dreamily, and almost weightlessly. A floating cloud, a stirring fish, a lost child.

He hovered his way around the house a few times and then drifted back to me. "Honey, I am ready."

"Ready for what?"

"I am ready to go home."

"But this is your home. We *are* home."

"Yes, honey, I know. But I mean the other home, you know what I mean."

"No, I don't know what you mean."

In the beginning, I didn't know what he meant. Did he mean one of the homes he had lived in previously? That would take us from Curtis,

Arkansas, his childhood home, to Arkadelphia; to Dallas, to Commerce, to Lubbock, in Texas; to Syracuse, New York; to State College, Pennsylvania; to DeKalb, Illinois; to El Paso, Dallas, Texas, the second time; to Manhasset, New York; to Coral Gables, Florida; to Old Westbury, New York; to Evanston, Illinois, again; and to Key Biscayne, Florida, again; before this final move to Big D, Texas, the charming third time.

All those homes might still be in his memory. Which one?

Where did he want to go? Where could he go? *Where could we go?*

Going home had been a daily tale almost every day for many years, sometimes late in the afternoon as soon as I stepped inside the house after returning from work, but more often in the evenings just as we had finished dinner, when all the chores were done and I was ready to relax. "Honey, I am ready to go home." One evening, after I had explained fifty or more times that we were home, but failed to make him accept that we *were* home, and after I had used various strategies to divert his attention, all to no avail, the unavoidable exhaustion and frustration set in. All my virtues escaped me: patience, rationality, sense of humor, tenacity, and strength. The decibels of my voice went from 55 dB to 125 dB, the level of an ambulance. In despair, I yelled, releasing a volley of words.

"I don't know where you want to go. *Go wherever you want to!*"

He fell silent. His silence made me feel guilty. He sensed my frustration but could neither remember nor understand what had made me scream at him. In his mind, every time he said, "Honey, I want to go home," it was the very first time he had said it.

But his silence was short lived. Less than five minutes later:

"Honey, I want to go home."

"We *are* home." I was still tense but better able to deal with the nonsense now.

"You know what I mean."

"Yes, I know what you mean, but do you know what you mean?" Sometimes, the teaser in me just wouldn't quit.

Maya Angelou remarked that "the ache for home lives in all of us, the safe place where we can go as we are and not be questioned."[6] Home is a safe place where we can be who we are and not be scrutinized. The desire for Home Sweet Home is so strong among people with Alzheimer's disease that this pleading to "go home" is quite common among them. Searching among their vanishing memories, they struggle to find a place where they feel safe and familiar, yet they often find none. Some speculate that it is their childhood home where they long to be, as the older memories stay longer, and they may have forgotten their more recent homes. Then do those who never left their childhood homes also want to "go home"? I wondered. Could the home they look for so untiringly be none other than a sense of familiarity and security, which, unfortunately, fades away as their memories fade?

Home Sweet Home, as we had known it, was gone.

And this was just the beginning. In the years to come, much more would be lost.

Home Sweet Home.

The Jim Thompson scarf hanging in the author's closet.

Three

HE WHO STEALS

The number one rule of thieves is that nothing is too small to steal.

—JIMMY BRESLIN, American author

ALMOST EVERY SOCIETY CREATES MORAL JUSTIFICATIONS for stealing. Most Chinese people know the story of Kong Yiji (孔乙己), the main character in Lu Xun's short story of the same name published in 1919. In the story, Kong Yiji is depicted as a poor vagrant who has failed the basic official examinations to qualify as a junior scholar (秀才); passing this exam was the first step toward obtaining a civil-service job in imperial China. He lacks any practical skills that could earn him a living and sometimes steals books to sell so he can buy a bowl of wine.

Kong Yiji (孔乙己).

"The purloining of volumes, good sir, cannot be counted as theft," he reasons. "The purloining of volumes is, after all, something that falls well within the purview of the scholarly life. How can it be considered mere theft?"[7]

"Stealing books cannot be counted as theft" (窃书不能算偷) thereafter became a popular Chinese saying, and the act of book-stealing is considered an elegant offense in Chinese culture.

There are further examples in Western culture. Victor Hugo's famous thief Jean Valjean, the protagonist of *Les Misérables*, spends nineteen years in prison for the theft of a loaf of bread to help feed his widowed sister and her seven children. He steals Bishop Myriel's silverware and silver plates despite the bishop's kindness in feeding and sheltering him. Valjean manages to win our affection. Robin Hood, famous in English folklore for stealing from the rich to give to the poor, elicits our deep admiration for noble deeds that fall outside the law.

These stories make us think further about circumstances in which stealing is morally acceptable or at least understandable. We sympathize with these thieves because of their vulnerability, and because of society's injustice. Yet, there are some stories of *stealing* that don't fit into any ethical thinking at all.

2004. Spring had returned to Dallas. Predictably, in front of the Ranchita house, the two pear-less Bradford pear trees were blooming again. Tiny white flowers covered the entire canopy of the trees, forming two near-perfect white spheres. Petals floated down like snowflakes, delicate, fragile, and ephemeral, covering the ground like a white blanket. A gentle breeze, the blanket was torn.

Inside the house, things started disappearing. First, small items: letter openers, scissors, my glasses; and little keepsakes that had been lying around the house: a Murano glass paperweight with geometric patterns, a Turkish evil eye with blue and gold circles, a Chinese jade statuette of intricately carved birds and chrysanthemums, a crystal ball of forgotten origin that was said to have healing power . . .

Was it the plump cleaning lady? The skinny plumber? The stern-faced exterminator? The smiling furniture-delivery man? The sweaty pool guy who had used the bathroom just the other day? Or maybe the bouncing kids next door whose curiosity might have led them astray when they came inside to shower after playing in our pool? The possibilities were endless, and everyone was a suspect. Even a few pots, pans, and dishes had vanished.

After some astute deductive logic, I concluded that the most likely culprit was none other than my darling husband.

"Clyde, have you seen my silk scarf? The Jim Thompson one you got for me in Bangkok the last time you went to Thailand?"

"What does it look like?"

"It looks like a scarf." It really did.

"Honey, you know what I mean." He saw humor neither in my response nor in his own question. "Where could you have put it?"

"I think I put it on the back of the chair by the breakfast table when I came home yesterday."

"Hon, don't worry. It's got to be somewhere in the house. Let me help you find it." He sounded earnest and innocent.

We looked in the bedroom closet, the hall closet, and all the guest bedroom closets; we checked behind the bathroom doors, the study doors, the living room doors, and all the other doors where a scarf could be hung. We searched the foyer, the kitchen, the various storage areas, the garage, and the car, where a logical or illogical mind might have left a scarf. I even peeked under beds, couches, dressers, chests, and any other furniture that a scarf might have slid under, voluntarily or involuntarily.

No scarf.

"Could you have left it in the office? Could someone have taken it?" Now he sounded concerned.

"Have you seen it? Did you put it away for me somewhere?"

Clyde liked to hang my clothes; he liked order. And I liked him putting my clothes away, in order. He complemented me. I was terribly absentminded and disorganized, leaving things everywhere in the house and losing them anywhere when I was out. I thought he had learned his organizational skills from the Air Force, but—as with other good habits— he gave most of the credit to his mother's training early in his life. But that was before his mind went south.

He thought for a while and found nothing in his memory. "No. I didn't."

"I am sure I left it in the kitchen, and there are only two of us," my rational mind opined.

Intellectually, I understood that in Clyde's Alzheimer's-damaged mind, all his odd behaviors seemed necessary. To quote the American film director

Samuel Fuller, "Being a hooker does not mean being evil. The same with a pickpocket, or even a thief. You do what you do out of necessity."[8] Yet, for me, the well spouse, accepting his illness and the irrationality it produced did not switch off my rational thinking the way one turns off a light switch. In my instinct to be rational, and in my desire to hold on to normality, to "get things right," I was sometimes driven to be relentless, to try to force "reality" onto Clyde despite his Alzheimer's.

"Clyde, why did you put this frying pan in your dresser drawer? You know that's not the place for it. What were you thinking when you did this?"

"I didn't do it. You know I didn't."

"There are only two of us. If you didn't do it, do you think I did it?"

"I don't know. Someone else could have done it." Clyde stared, puzzled, at the greasy frying pan occupying most of the space in the drawer, nesting awkwardly on top of his pile of clean white Hanes.

"Who? Was anyone else in the house while I was gone?"

"There could have been. There are other people. I think you know some of them."

Clyde had once been an eloquent speaker. In high school, he was a member of the debate team. His debate coach said that his voice resembled that of Jimmy Stewart. And, with that Jimmy Stewart–like voice, without "practice and practice," he had performed brilliantly not only on the debate team but eventually also on the stage of Carnegie Hall, where he delivered numerous graduation speeches as president of Baruch College in Manhattan, which held its commencement ceremonies there during his tenure at Baruch.[1] That Jimmy Stewartlike voice had always been able to make convincing arguments, most times logically, sometimes not.

"But who? Who would come to our house and take our things? It doesn't make any sense." I was not ready to give in to irrationality.

"That, those . . . people."

Of course he couldn't name the names. "You know I wouldn't do it." Now he was defensive. "Honey, are you unhappy with me? Why is it always my fault?" Now I could hear the hurt in his voice.

The rational and irrational worlds are often at war. For people not afflicted with cognitive impairment, the mind produces rational thought and argument, as well as logical plans and decisions, as a matter of course. Accepting the irrational arguments or behavior of an Alzheimer's patient often involves considerable effort and awareness of what is happening. It often requires that the well spouse alter his or her own thinking and behavior. During the early years of my caregiving journey, the struggle frequently left me feeling upset, frustrated, exhausted, guilty, or angry. For a spousal caregiver, feelings are often intensified by seemingly insurmountable physical and financial demands coupled with emotional suffering. When we make our wedding vows, "for better or for worse, in sickness and in health," how many of us are really prepared for the possibility of a long caregiving journey through years or even decades of chronic illness?

In his book *The Forgetting: Alzheimer's: Portrait of an Epidemic*, David Shenk records the struggle and transformation of N. B. from Merrimack, New Hampshire, a well spouse: "I have really struggled with the honesty issue." N. B. lists all the "fabricated" events and imagined crises the ill person's delusional mind has insisted are happening, and he observes: "I couldn't find any reason for telling her over and over that she has a horrible terrible degenerating disease that was making her feel the way she does. . . . It may feel better for me to verbalize the facts, but what she needs is comfort and security—not the truth. The truth won't change anything."[10]

Shenk also writes about the experience of Rolfe S. from Fairfield, Vermont, who admits that early on, he tried to make his wife, Phyllis, live the "normal" way, as in their pre-Alzheimer's life. That effort made both of them agitated and unhappy. Then he realized that if, instead of scolding her, he "thanked her for bringing the frying pan into the bathroom, . . . life changed very much for the good."[11]

Just like N. B. and Rolfe S., I eventually stopped ruffling my husband's feathers. Instead, I adjusted and assimilated into the strange world of an Alzheimer's mind, where illusion and distortion had become reality. This transition took time, patience, persistence, and, most importantly, conscious effort on my part. Gradually, I formed a new paradigm of living in which I was able, most of the time, to face the chaos calmly, and even to laugh at the absurdity of Clyde's world—*our world.*

Stealing, or, more accurately, hoarding, is a common behavior among people with Alzheimer's disease, usually during the early to middle stages of the illness. Stealing generally implies taking other people's things knowing that these things don't belong to them. But Alzheimer's patients often have no awareness that the things they have taken do not belong to them. They often have no recollection of what is in the hoard and where the hoarded goods have been hidden. Research shows that about a quarter to a third of dementia patients display such behavior. Although the pathology behind it is not clear, researchers speculate that the presence of things provides comfort and a sense of security to Alzheimer's patients who are experiencing isolation as their memory loss impacts their relationships with family and friends; they may feel that everything familiar is slipping away. They hoard in order to hold on to something. It is also common that in the delusional, paranoid mind of Alzheimer's patients, other people are trying to steal from them. Hoarding often goes along with hiding things, not because they know that these are stolen goods, but because they are afraid that others will take them away.

One Saturday morning I was helping Clyde organize his file cabinets, something he had guarded tightly until that moment. Upon unlocking and opening them, I uncovered his secret treasure trove. Here in the drawers I found not only the Jim Thompson scarf but also the letter opener, some scissors, several pairs of glasses, the Italian glass paperweight, the Turkish evil eye, the Chinese jade carving, the crystal ball of forgotten origin, and much more.

Over the years, things found in our trash cans and wastebaskets included glasses, a cell phone, a remote control, and keys; under the bed were newspapers and books; inside the dresser drawers were dishes. And, oh, Clyde's pockets! Things frequently emerging from there included socks, with or without their mates; tissues, clean or gently used; stained rags; unpaid bills, unopened invitations, and unanswered telephone messages he had taken; and letters. To my horror, among the letters were some addressed to neighbors. Apparently he had taken them from their mailboxes. To my delight, there were also a couple of checks waiting to be cashed. He stuffed his pockets with such zeal that he must have felt quite exasperated when he couldn't squeeze in one more used tissue.

Clyde's "stealing" and hiding behavior lasted several years in the course of his disease. While he lived at home, he occasionally stole the neighbors' mail and garbage cans. In his adult day-care center, he stole books, playing cards, men's caps, and women's scarves. In an assisted-living facility where he spent part of a year, he stocked his room with goods he had taken from other people's rooms: women's clothes, cushions, cups, toothbrushes, and towels. One day when I was visiting him there, I fetched out of his bulging pocket an XXXL-sized bra!

It would have been futile to tell Clyde that these were not his things and that taking other people's possessions was not nice. He would admit to no wrongdoing. He did what he did out of his perceived necessity. And he was *honest*.

One spring afternoon in 2006, Clyde's fourth year of living with Alzheimer's disease, my beautiful friend Dolly and her new boyfriend, Ken, a tall, handsome, smartly dressed car salesman, came to visit us in our new home in University Park. "Barbie and Ken," as I teasingly nicknamed them, were chatting in the living room with me while Clyde sat with us, quietly listening and trying to comprehend. In the middle of the conversation, Ken stood up and walked to Clyde. "Clyde, can I borrow your cell phone?"

"Sure," said Clyde. He fumbled inside his pocket and fished out a cell phone.

"Why do you need to borrow his cell phone?" I was puzzled. Didn't Handsome Ken have his own? Why couldn't he borrow his Barbie's or mine?

"Thank you." Ken took the phone from Clyde, smiled, and in a matter-of-fact manner, held it up to show me.

In Handsome Ken's hand was his own cell phone.

The author with her friend "Barbie."

Charlie and Ronnie at LifeWalk, an annual advocacy event for people living with
HIV/AIDS, Turtle Creek Park, Dallas, Texas, 2008.

Four

QUEENS AND QUEERS

All the world is queer save thee and me,
And even thou art a little queer.

—Robert Owen (1771–1858),
Welsh social reformer and a founder of utopian socialism

It was a Sunday early in the summer of 2004. I woke up from my queenly beauty sleep at nine thirty. Around the edge of the curtain, I could see the Texas sun, high and bright, happily bathing my corner of the Lone Star land with its warmth. Clyde had already been up for a while. I knew that by this time he would have had his breakfast, two slices of plain whole wheat toast washed down with plain black coffee: unassuming and unexciting. Now he would be sitting at the kitchen table with the *Wall Street Journal*, nursing his cup of joe.

"Mmmm!" I stretched as far as I could. Nothing was more physically satisfying than a full stretch after a long, deep sleep, not even sex. I started to sing loudly and off-key in my raucous voice, knowing I would get Clyde's attention.

"Sunshine on my shoulder makes me happy. Sunshine on my shoulder makes me cry." I was improvising, making the "a" in "make" very long.

The bedroom door was slightly ajar and then slowly opened wide. In came Clyde, cup of coffee in hand.

"Makes me 'high,' not 'cry.'" Clyde proceeded to give me a kiss in bed. He set his coffee on the dresser and pulled the curtains open to let the light in.

"But I want to cry," I exerted my individuality, "because I am so haaappeee. . . ."

Before I could finish, a strong burning smell struck my nostrils.

"What's that smell?" I sprang out of bed. "Baby, are you cooking something?"

Clyde turned toward the kitchen, and I followed right behind him. In the kitchen, the toaster oven was shooting out smoke, and the smoke had already permeated the kitchen. Clyde rushed to the toaster. He bent down to look inside and, at the same time, opened the door. Blaze leaped out and pounced on his face, sending him reeling. With a giant stride, I dashed forward, grabbed his arm, pushed him aside, and quickly shut the toaster door.

"Keep the door closed!" I barked. "Don't let the air in."

I unplugged the toaster. Grabbing Clyde by the hand, I took him outside to the patio to check his face in the sunlight. He looked stunned. "What just happened?" Rubbing his face in puzzlement, he didn't utter any words but seemed to be asking, "Something happened. My face feels funny."

Clyde had put two pieces of bread in the toaster oven for me, leaving them to come into the bedroom when he heard my singing. The toaster oven didn't turn itself off like the simpler toasters. Luckily, the casualty to Clyde was superficial. He had lost the remaining of his already thin eyebrows and all his eyelashes, and some hair on his forehead. His whiskers would have suffered a massive loss had he not been clean-shaven. And it could have been much worse.

The time has come to Clyde-proof the house, because my horse, Clyde the

Clydesdale, is confused, I thought to myself while opening the windows and doors to let out the smoke.

Over the next couple of weeks, I performed a safety overhaul. I replaced the toaster oven with a two-slice toaster that required pressing just one lever to operate and was smart enough to shut itself off. I switched the complicated programmable coffee maker for the simplest one-touch model that happened to be the cheapest on the market. To keep Clyde from turning on the burners or oven, I removed the control knobs from the range. I traded the stovetop kettle for an electric one that automatically cut off to heat water for tea; I placed green and red dot stickers on the microwave, television remotes, and thermostat to remind Clyde where the on and off buttons were, green for on, red for off; and I rearranged furniture so there were no potential obstacles when he walked around the house.

To ensure that Clyde could reach other family members and me easily, I programmed one-touch numbers into his cell phone. I told him that the numbers were based on no-nonsense Texas logic: "Don't mess with Texas women!" It went like this: I used "5" for myself, his center of attention; "4" for his sister and "6" for his daughter, to keep all of us women at the center of his universe; then "3" for his brother and "7" for his son, because men were at the outskirts to protect their women. He liked my idea, thinking I was serious. I reminded Clyde to keep his cell phone with him whenever he was out walking. It would be his lifeline if he got lost. He seemed to understand the importance and always held on to this little gadget tightly.

For some reason, Clyde developed a fixation on the number "3." He kept pushing "3" and asking for me.

"Dr. Lan, please." He thought he was calling my office.

"Clyde, are you looking for JoAnn?" On the other end was a baritone voice very much like his, coming from his younger brother. "This is Joe."

"Oh, Joe. Do you know where JoAnn is?"

"I think she is at work. I am in Washington, DC."

"Oh. I didn't know you were in Washington, DC. What are you doing there?"

"I am working with a client right now." Joe is an attorney. He didn't explain that he had been in Washington, DC for the past four decades.

"Where are you? I will ask JoAnn to call you."

"I am taking a walk. I don't know where I am. Can JoAnn come and get me?"

So Joe called me, and I called Clyde. But Clyde didn't know where he was in the neighborhood. Fortunately, I knew Clyde the Clydesdale was a creature of habit. Driving slowly, I combed the streets of the neighborhood tracing his usual routes until I spotted the lost horse, walking alone with a serious face and at an earnest pace, as if he had a board meeting to attend, location unknown.

Yes, it was definitely time to get help for Clyde during the long hours while I was at work and he was home alone.

I put an ad in the local Chinese newspaper. After chatting with a few applicants, I hired our first helper, Wang, a Chinese woman. But Clyde protested. "I don't want a stranger in the house when I'm at home. I am a very private person."

"Let's try it for one week. If you are just not comfortable with her, I promise we will stop," I coaxed, doubting my own sincerity.

Many Chinese people consider Western-style food unpalatable: uncooked vegetables; bloody flesh, as in a piece of medium-rare steak; cold cuts; smelly cheeses; oily cakes laden with sugar and artificial colors. Wang rejected all Western food and quickly decided that Clyde's usual lunch, a sandwich with cold cuts or a bowl of Cheerios with fruit, nuts, and milk, was unacceptable.

"Not so good to eat." Staring at Clyde's sandwich, Wang declared with great certainty, "Cold food bad for tummy. Make you bellyache." I heard this claim about cold food and bellyache throughout my childhood.

Wang's husband, a chef in a Chinese restaurant, regularly took home an abundance of Chinese dishes. She brought a selection of these to our house for her own lunch. There were endless stir-fried meats and vegetables, fried or steamed dumplings, and rice, which Clyde the Southern boy loved. She shared her lunch proudly and generously with

Clyde. How could anyone resist trading a salad for a dish of Gong Pao chicken over steamed rice, or sacrificing a cold sandwich for crispy fried dumplings dripping with soy sauce and sesame oil?

Whether it was the superiority of Wang's lunches or the inferiority of my husband's memory of my one-week-trial promise, by the end of the first week, Clyde no longer protested Wang's presence in the house. However, he refused to let Wang accompany him on his walks. Most of the time they stayed out of each other's way in the house, which was big enough for a platoon. Wang worked mostly in the kitchen, laundry room, bathrooms, living room, or other parts of the house. Clyde stayed in our bedroom, where he had a small desk by the window facing the backyard and swimming pool. He spent hours trying very hard to balance his checkbook, figure out his retirement accounts, trace his stock portfolio, organize his contacts and calendar, or remember what he was looking for at the moment. It was, overall, an arrangement that worked well for both of them.

Wang, however, was a strong-willed woman who had a very precise view of what was the correct way of life. In her mind, salads had no nutritional value, and cold milk was indigestible. Dishwashers didn't clean dishes, and detergent was dangerously poisonous. Washing machines damaged clothes, dryers consumed too much electricity, vacuum cleaners didn't clean properly, and air conditioners made people sick. The floors were too light to keep clean, and the whole house was too big to be livable. As the list went on, I felt more and more displaced and rejected in my own home. *But Clyde is safer, and he likes the good lunches. And I like the peace of mind and coming home to a clean house,* I told myself. *Nobody is perfect.*

Months went by. In the winter of 2005, the new house we had been building in University Park was ready. We moved out of our house on Ranchita to our new home in University Park. The move itself took the whole of one very long day, and Wang did her best to look after Clyde while I worked with the moving crew.

One day soon after the move, I bought some white porcelain bowls. They were big and sturdy, good for the one-bowl meals we had come to favor in our effort to simplify our eating habits. And so reasonably priced! I showed Wang my shopping trophies, proudly showing off my aesthetic sensibility and economic prudence.

"*Aya!*" Wang exclaimed. "No good. Too big and too heavy."

"I want big bowls. It will be easy for us, just one bowl each to carry and wash."

"How could you buy something like this?" As she rinsed them, she continued her disapproving remarks while smacking her mouth and shaking her head. "They look ugly."

Chinese people don't always know how to be tactful in expressing their dissatisfaction.

"They may not be the best looking, but I don't think they look bad." I tried to stand my ground.

"*Made in China.* Look!" She turned a bowl over and showed me the mark on the bottom, which of course I had already seen. Many Chinese loathed things made in China. To them, it was the synonym of "poor quality."

"That doesn't bother me. I bought them at a good price."

"Take them back. You must take them back." She flagrantly ignored my comments. "You can return them, you know?"

I had been an inflated balloon flying high and happy a moment ago, but now I felt punctured and depressed. I might be the queen of this house, but Wang was the Empress of China! And I was not going to go backward into the Chinese past.

Spring came. Wang went back to China to visit family there. I moved on to the next helper, a pleasant, soft-spoken African American woman, Tiara. Quite tall and equally impressive in width, she was a paramount statue, a veritably queenly figure.

We met at a Starbucks, and I offered her a Venti latte, which looked disproportionately small in her hand. After we exchanged pleasantries and background information about each other, we shifted to talking about the job, her experience, and my expectations, which all went well. Finally, I spilled out the question that had been on my mind. "Are you able to climb stairs? All the bedrooms and the laundry room in my house are upstairs."

"Yes." She breathed heavily, as if she were already climbing the stairs. "No problem."

Tiara had a tragic story to tell. She had been a single mother raising a teenage son. One day, her son was taking the garbage out and was shot dead by neighborhood gang members. "He was a good kid," she said. "He was not in a gang."

I have always found it difficult to know how to comfort someone who has experienced that kind of loss. It seemed to me that at that moment words would only trivialize what had happened. Before Clyde came into my life, I had been a single mother raising a son in a foreign land. I was proud of having earned every penny with my own hands to support us. Tiara had my sympathy for the tragedy in her life and my respect for her desire to be an independent woman, earning a living to support her family. *We could be supportive of each other.* What was more, she was a native speaker of English, which would make communicating with Clyde easier.

Tiara resigned after barely a week without giving me any reason, leaving me with the memory of her astonishing queenly figure struggling up and down the stairs, breathing hard; and with relief from my constant worry that she might lose her balance on my stairs.

After Tiara we tried a white woman, whose name I have forgotten, and then another white woman, whose name I have also forgotten. Clyde was not interested in the conversations they tried to engage him in, nor in the TV shows they decided to put on for him, nor in the food they prepared, nor in their attempts to accompany him on walks, and he definitely wouldn't let them help him use the bathroom.

"Honey, I don't want a stranger in my house," Clyde said, as he had told me when I hired Wang. "It makes me uncomfortable."

Each of these women left at the end of her weeklong trial period. No real connection had been established between any of the caregivers and their charge.

I posted another help wanted ad on Craigslist. This time, among the promising applicants was a young Hispanic woman, Rosa Maria. Just eighteen years old, she was petite, pretty, and energetic. I liked the idea of having a caregiver who was fit and agile. Furthermore, like me, Rosa Maria was an immigrant woman who had come to this land of opportunity to better her life.

"Don't worry. I will take care of *abuelito*," Rosa Maria assured me.

I can be a good role model for her, I thought to myself.

The first day young Rosa Maria came to work, she wore a skimpy top that exposed all of her shoulders, most of her cleavage, and much of her midriff; and a pair of shorts so short that I was nervous that with each movement, the cheeks of her bum would hang out. She had gorgeous cleavage, promising the firm softness of what was to follow. *Do women with modest curves, women who come from vegetable-eating traditions, feel subconsciously intimidated by and envious of the bold, voluptuous women of the meat- and cheese-eating traditions?* I wondered, thinking of myself and my race. Rosa Maria's clothing was mildly shocking for an older and old-fashioned Chinese woman like me. In my younger years in China, modesty had been my only dress code, and I had never been able to break that code, even now that I lived in a culture with much more relaxed attitudes.

Rosa Maria was not a queen or an empress. I saw her rather as a mermaid, a Lorelei, as in Heinrich Heine's poem "Die Lorelei":

> She holds a golden comb,
> Singing along, as well
> An enthralling
> And spellbinding melody.
>
> In his little boat, the boatman
> Is seized by it with a savage woe.
> He does not look upon the rocky ledge
> But rather high up into the heavens.[12]

A statue of Lorelei by the Rhine River.

Should I worry about the boatman and his boat being devoured by the waves? Should I worry about my Clyde, confused and vulnerable, succumbing to the power of Lorelei's spellbinding melody?

But I was not going to let my imaginary problem deprive us of the possibility of hiring an excellent caregiver. Rosa Maria was smart and a fast learner. When Clyde went for his walks, she did not insist on going with him; instead, she trailed him closely to keep an eye on him. She did the chores I asked her to do. She was likable and had a kind of cleverness in her. Clyde didn't complain profusely about Rosa Maria, as he had about the other women, either because she was easy on the eyes or, more likely, because she shrewdly stayed out of Clyde's sight most of the time. When I stopped by home to check on Clyde, Rosa Maria would emerge from somewhere in the house, and Clyde was often not aware that she was there at all.

One day in the spring of 2005, Clyde's daughter Joy and her children, Collin and Gabby, came to visit. After lunch, the adults were sitting downstairs around the kitchen island, chatting and laughing. I looked around for Rosa Maria. *Perhaps she could take abuelito to the bathroom?*

"Has anyone seen Rosa Maria?" I asked. "Maybe Clyde needs to go to the bathroom now."

"We haven't seen her for a while," Joy said.

"Is Rosa Maria with you guys?" I called across the hallway to the living room, where Collin and Gabby were watching TV.

"No," two voices called back simultaneously.

I was about to take Clyde to the bathroom myself but stopped. I had an idea.

"I have often wondered what Rosa Maria does upstairs. Let's get Collin to go upstairs and find out," I told Joy with a mischievous smile.

"Col, dear, come here," Joy called out to her son, who came right in. "Can you go up to Grandpa's room and get his green sweater from the closet?"

"Sure."

"And see where Rosa Maria is and what she is doing, but quietly." She lowered her voice and threw me a wink. All three of us smiled furtively. We were partners in crime on a reconnaissance project.

Collin soon came downstairs carrying his grandpa's old green cashmere sweater. "She is sitting on JoAnn's bed, clipping her toenails and painting them."

"Did she see you?" Joy asked, with the smile of a girl who did something terrible and didn't want to be caught.

"Yes, she did."

"Did she say anything?"

"Nothing. She didn't care."

Lorelei the Mermaid didn't last very long after that. She left for a more action-filled job, cleaning houses with her cousins.

The boatman might be safe, but the horse was still confused. What now?

Over the course of a year, between summer 2004 and summer 2005, we went through a string of rainbow-colored caregivers of all types and various ethnicities and backgrounds. For many reasons, none worked out. One day in June 2005, I skimmed through the jobs wanted section of the classified pages of the *Dallas Observer*, a free weekly publication, and called a few prospects. One caller sounded particularly promising. For the past several years, she had been taking care of an elderly woman who had just passed away. She had been caring for older people for over a decade, was familiar with administering medications, and knew how to use basic medical equipment. She had her own car and spoke *authentic* English, at least to me—she even had a strong Texas accent. Some of her vowels were drawn out and slightly distorted. For example, instead of saying, "I am leaving it in the den for you," she would say "Ah'm layving it in the dayn for ya." The Southern accent sounded sweet and pleasant, but there seemed to be a trace of masculinity in her voice, and I thought that I heard that she said her name was Charles. But in English, a name is hardly a certainty of a person's gender. I knew women named Sam and men named Pat.

Could she, in fact, be a he? We agreed upon meeting the next afternoon at one o'clock.

The following day, right at the appointed time, a car slowly pulled up in front of my house. A man got out on the passenger side. The doorbell rang, and I opened the door to let in a tall, handsome man who looked to be in his fifties. The mystery of the voice became clear: it was a man with a somewhat feminine-sounding voice, not the other way around. But I was still slightly surprised. I was not expecting a man in this line of work. I was not sure if men could be good caregivers, and I wondered if it would be difficult for me to work with a man: Would he accept me as the supreme queen-commander as well as devote himself to the mundane and petty tasks of caregiving?

"Hi, Mrs. Wingfield? I am Charles Beebe." His voice had the same sweetness and lightly elevated pitch I had heard on the phone. "We talked yesterday."

Hiding my surprise and my doubts, I calmly led him to the family room to sit on the couch with Clyde and me. To my delight, shortly after Charles and I started to talk, Clyde chimed in. He and Charles traded stories about rural Texas, where both of them had spent their youth. During the two decades or so that separated their younger years, rural Texas had not changed much. They traced their respective family roots in the Southwest, in places separated by some distance geographically but not too far apart in terms of culture. They both had American Indian heritage: Clyde had some Shawnee and Cherokee blood, and Charles's mother was a Cherokee.

The conversation went on pleasantly and lasted longer than I had expected, way beyond the scope of a routine job interview for a caregiver. Then I suddenly remembered that someone had driven Charles here.

"Did someone bring you today?" I tilted my head toward the street where the car was parked. "Why don't you invite him in, or is it her? It's boiling outside."

"My brother drove may hayre," Charles said softly. "Hay's fine thayre."

"No, no." I insisted. "It's too hot. This is Texas summer. He shouldn't be sitting in the car for such a long time."

Charles went out. He soon came in with a man a few years younger and a few inches shorter than he, equally good-looking, though in a very different way.

"This is my brother Ronald." Charles introduced us, and we shook hands with him.

It turned out that Ronald was a graduate of Southern Methodist University, where I was employed. My first impression of Ronald was that he was quiet. He sat on the chair next to the couch, hardly opening his mouth while Charles, Clyde, and I continued our casual conversation. How deceptive that first impression was, as we would soon find out.

And the minute I laid eyes on the two of them together, I knew they were not brothers.

Just like that, Charlie and Ronnie, the queers, as they sometimes affectionately referred to each other, came into our lives. For much of my journey as a well spouse, from the summer of 2005 until the fall of 2011 when Clyde passed away, they were my comrades, shoulder to shoulder with me in the battle with Clyde's Alzheimer's disease. Little did I know how many twists and turns would be ahead of us, and how many hurdles we would have to overcome. They became part of my family, and we were there for each other, they for me, and I for them, through all the ups and downs in our lives. Just like that, the lives of two gay men from Texas and a straight woman from Shanghai became intimately entwined.

Charlie and Ronnie in front of their home, taken before the author had met them.

Clyde and Charlie in Dallas Arboretum, 2006.

Five

THE BIRD A NEST

When I look at the world, I'm pessimistic,
but when I look at people, I am optimistic.

—CARL ROGERS, American psychologist (1902–1987)

APRIL 15, 2011, WAS AN ORDINARY MORNING in my long journey as a well spouse. Charlie had just arrived for the day. As I came downstairs, I could hear his sweet voice singing: "Bill on the still hill drinks a bucket or two. . . ." Charlie told me it was an old Texas Hill Country tune, but I have not been able to verify its origin.[13]

I loved to hear Charlie sing. His voice had a broad range. He sometimes used falsetto for high notes, which sounded sweet. He sang so beautifully that he was often invited to sing at weddings and funerals for family and friends. Somehow, hearing his singing in the house reassured me that things were OK, and if they were not, I had his strong shoulder to lean on.

"You have good days, and you have bad days," Charlie said to me when I felt especially blue. "Just think that tomorrow will be a good day."

It worked for me. Hope has the magic power to make the unbearable bearable.

I went into the family room next to the kitchen and approached Clyde, who was lying on his hospital bed against one wall. He was awake. His eyes, so hollow that I couldn't see the bottom of them, followed the movements of my face but were unfocused and showed no sign of recognition. He no longer smiled. I rubbed his face and smoothed his hair gently, believing that somehow, in a remote part of his consciousness, he would get my message telling him that he was safe and loved.

"Clyde, did you sleep well?" Charlie still talked to Clyde, although Clyde had stopped responding a long time ago. He pulled off Clyde's blanket, and I reached underneath to feel the diaper pad.

Wet, big time!

Charlie unfastened the diaper and folded it around Clyde's waist, turned his body toward the wall, and held him there while I bent down, tightly rolled up the pad, heavy with still-warm liquid, and dragged it out from underneath Clyde. My face was right by Clyde's behind.

"That was a big one!" I said to Charlie. "At least he didn't blow out a lot of gas right into my face."

We had worked out this routine and performed it seamlessly every day. Afterward Charlie wiped Clyde down and changed him, and I fed Clyde his breakfast.

It had been almost nine years since Clyde's diagnosis of Alzheimer's disease in late 2002, and almost six years since Charlie and Ronnie came to us on that hot June afternoon in 2005.

It must have been only a few weeks after Charlie and Ronnie entered our lives that I asked them to call us by our first names. Being called "Mr. Wingfield" and "Mrs. Wingfield" seemed far too formal.

"Mrs. Wingfield, what say you?" an imaginary judge with a wig that looked very artificial asked in a guttural voice, as in a British television courtroom drama.

"Your Honor, I'd like to plead the Fifth," a Mrs. Wingfield responded. Or maybe she would say, *"No comment,"* as "plead the Fifth" is used only in the US?

Clyde chimed in, "Yes, it's about time you guys stopped calling me Mr. Wingfield. Call me Clyde. I insist." Charlie referred to all his previous employers, and to others for whom he had been a caregiver, by their last names with the proper prefixes. To me, this form of address seemed old-fashioned and unnecessary now that Charlie and Ronnie were in my family handling the most intimate details of our daily life, such as taking Clyde to the latrine and laundering our undergarments. After some initial hesitation, they accepted our request, and soon we were all on a first-name basis.

I asked Charlie if I could call him "Charlie" instead of Charles, since he was not the Prince of England. "Yes, it ain't matter to me." So Charles was Charlie to Clyde and me, Chuck to Ronnie, and Charles to everyone else.

And Ronnie? He was just Ronnie, except when we were annoyed with him, and then he was Ronald.

Charlie and Ronnie looked so different that even a fool wouldn't believe they were brothers. Charlie later told me that he hadn't wanted to shock me by telling me on the first day we met that he was gay. Well, he had underestimated this Chinese woman. My life had included so many shocks that I was more or less shockproof. At five feet eleven inches, Charlie was tall and lean with well-proportioned limbs. Ronnie told me that Charlie had once been a dancer in a nightclub, a part of his history that Charlie didn't want to reveal to anyone. Underneath his blond hair was a sculpted face with high cheekbones, a strong chin, a "foreign devil's" big nose, and a set of blue eyes under heavy blond brows.[14] He looked German to me, but he was actually the son of a man of Scottish ancestry and a Cherokee woman. He must have inherited those high cheekbones from his mother. Ronnie was just five feet six inches tall, short and round, evidently an overachiever nutritionally. His dark brown eyes flickered under long dark eyelashes. His dark hair was tightly curled, his face smooth and tanned. The only feature they had in common was that both wore mustaches that matched their respective hair color.

"I am not black," Ronnie was quick to clarify, referring to his dark hair with tiny curls.

I thought both of them were good-looking, and I let them know. Charlie said nothing, but Ronnie was visibly pleased. They smiled at each other as if they were hiding a few secrets. I later learned that they had enhanced their appearance: hair dyed, skin moisturized and spray-tanned, nails polished. I had heard that, as a general rule, gay men were more particular about their appearance. I wished all men were like that.

I quickly realized that Ronnie was not the quiet one, as I had mistakenly assumed after our first encounter. In fact, no one could stop Ronald Duck from quacking. Within a matter of days, I learned every detail of his entire life, which spanned almost five decades. He was a graduate of Southern Methodist University, the "rich kids' school," and had grown up a rich kid indeed. His daddy owned three "car lots," aka car dealerships, in Big D. Ronnie was the youngest boy in the family and was spoiled rotten. His mother adored her baby boy. She took him along to the best restaurants and shops and lavished on him all kinds of things, beyond his heart's desire. Her wealthy women friends doted on him. His parents gave him fancy cars and pushed him into marrying a very young woman, believing that doing so would "cure" his "deviant" sexuality. They paid his wife a generous stipend to stay married to him, but the marriage didn't last.

After Ronnie's father died, his mother eventually became ill with Alzheimer's disease and went to live with one of his sisters. His siblings would not allow him to see his mother anymore, and they all rejected him utterly. Was it because of his homosexuality, his in-your-face attitude, past jealousy over his being their mom and dad's favorite, or all of these? I didn't know. But Ronnie didn't care. He had his Chuck.

Charlie, on the other hand, was a country boy who had grown up on a farm in a rural Texas town. He was the middle child among eleven siblings, three boys and eight girls, all from the same heroic mother. From early boyhood, while his father was away in the army, he helped his mother, a domineering Cherokee woman who was the commander in chief of the household. Charlie plowed fields, planted and harvested crops, helped with household chores, and took care of his younger siblings. Every pair of hands had to work so they could feed all those mouths with their scarce resources.

Rural communities in the 1960s and 1970s were even more conservative than they are today, especially in the Texas countryside. Homosexuals were generally not accepted, and their families often felt ashamed. So Charlie hid his sexual orientation from his conservative, devoutly religious family long after he had left home, until one day, when he was in his late thirties, he brought Ronnie to a family reunion with no warning and no explanation. Charlie's mother and siblings couldn't believe that their handsome, God-fearing Charles was gay. They blamed Ronnie for leading Charlie astray. Although Charlie's family never rejected Charlie himself, they never accepted Ronnie, who, in his typical flamboyant manner, openly let everyone know that their Charlie was just as gay as he was and that both were superior to their redneck and unenlightened relatives.

Ronnie was clearly smart. Like most smart people, he did not suffer fools gladly. Once, when he was waiting tables at a restaurant, he served an elderly lady a sandwich. The lady looked at the sandwich on her plate and said, "But I told you that I wanted the mustard to be on top of the meat." Ronnie picked up the sandwich on the plate and flipped it over. "Here you have it." He had the pleasure of watching the lady gaping at the plate, speechless.

During their courtship, Ronnie was a funeral director, a job he loved. He would drive a stately black Cadillac hearse to pick Charlie up after work. The two lovers would spend their evenings in the funeral home, making up the dead. Older women were their favorite. They groomed each woman's hair; applied lipstick, blush, nail polish, and fake eyelashes; then dressed her up for her big event the next day, the wake or funeral. Charlie would say to her softly, "Sweetheart, I am going to make you so *perty*." And he always did.

And he would sing a *bluegrassy* gospel song:

> Down here my burden's heavy
> And the road is rough and long
> Sometimes my feet get weary and so sore
> But a brighter day is coming
> Soon I'll step on Heaven's shore
> And I won't have to worry anymore[15]

It was such a sweet song, made sweeter by Charlie's mellow and somewhat feminine voice and softened by his drawn-out vowels. Every time Charlie sang it in the house, its melancholy tune moved me. Later, at Clyde's funeral service in 2011, I asked Charlie to sing this song with a twist, changing all the first-person pronouns to second person.

> Soon *you*'ll step on Heaven's shore
> And *you* won't have to worry anymore

Once I knew that there was a genuine bond of affection among us, it was safe for me to ask Charlie and Ronnie a potentially offensive question:

"From what I have observed, it seems that homosexual couples always have one person who is more masculine and one who is more feminine, like a man and a woman in a heterosexual couple. So which one of you is the man and which one is the w—"

Before I could finish the question, Ronnie responded.

"I am a man and he is a man. That's what makes us a gay couple."

It was an unexpected answer, but it sure made sense. Ronnie said that was the question most often asked of them and also the most ridiculous question. That made sense too.

At the time Charlie started working for us, Ronnie was on the night shift in a hospital, filing medical insurance forms. After work, he went home to take a nap, then came to our house early in the afternoon and stayed until Charlie had finished, usually by around five in the evening.

While Charlie was working in the house, Ronnie kept Clyde company. One day I came home from the university and found Ronnie talking to Clyde. He was pouring out a stream of frustrations about his job: how the managers wouldn't listen to him, wouldn't believe him, didn't understand, didn't care, and wouldn't talk to one of his colleagues as Ronnie had asked them to do, and how the colleague wouldn't admit that some problem had arisen because of a mistake she'd made, and how she wouldn't correct the mistake herself but expected Ronnie to fix it, and how she thought she was above him, and how unfair it all was, and how he knew that he was definitely right.

Clyde, who at the time could still understand some conversations, listened attentively and even asked a few questions for clarification. Finally, Ronnie was finished. With the same seriousness that he would have used if he were counseling a member of his senior executive team, the former university president said, "Ronnie, I have some advice for you."

Ronnie had been venting, and Clyde was his only willing ear. He wondered what meaningful advice Clyde could offer in his diminished mental condition.

"OK," he said, politely and expectantly.

Clyde licked his lips as he always did when trying to squeeze out the words, and finally said solemnly, "Don't be crucified on small crosses."

Ronnie laughed. It made wonderful sense. He saw right away that it was his own pettiness that was bothering him, and his frustration evaporated. "Don't be crucified on small crosses" became our favorite motto from that day on.

Unfortunately, we would eventually witness the exhaustion of Clyde's pearls of wisdom. Several years later, Ronnie was again telling one of those long, convoluted stories about this person and that person, and who did what to whom, what happened after that, who said what to whom, who was happy and who was not, who was right and who was wrong.... He talked for over half an hour without pausing for breath. Charlie and I were listening, or pretending to listen, and Clyde was sitting with us. When Ronnie was done at last, Charlie and I looked at each other and breathed a sigh of relief.

Sensing that the conversation was over, Clyde stood up, walked over to Ronnie's side, and put his arm around Ronnie's shoulders. We all looked at Clyde, wondering what he was about to do. Clyde paused, leaned slightly toward Ronnie licking his lips, and stuttered:

"Could you, could you, could you . . ." He was searching for the words, and we all held our breath, waiting.

"Take it from the top!"

The three of us looked at each other for a moment in disbelief, then simultaneously burst into laughter. For once, Ronald Duck was tired of quacking, and we were spared his repeating the entire story again.

Charlie and Ronnie had been a couple for seventeen years by the time they came to us. Even though their personalities were like night and day, they were still inseparable. Charlie was quiet, and Ronnie was talkative; Charlie was somewhat shy, while Ronnie was flamboyant; Charlie was thrifty, but Ronnie never hesitated before walking into the most expensive stores, whether or not he had any money; Charlie was sweet, and Ronnie was always in your face in a way that was annoying and amusing at the same time. Charlie worked nonstop to keep Clyde safe,

Celebrating Ronnie's birthday in the big-and-beautiful house, 2008.

the house clean, and me happy. And Ronnie? Always quacking, being annoying, entertaining us, not lifting a finger.

"You are not my boss," Ronnie would say to me as he sat on the couch with Clyde, talking cheerfully about anything and everything, munching on snacks, and drinking the eleventh of the fifteen cans of diet soda he poured down his throat every day.

Well, Ronnie, you are doing my job, just not getting paid.

For a long period of time, Clyde's restlessness was the most frustrating challenge. Although his body was still strong and healthy, he was no longer able to read, a lifelong passion of his, nor could he comprehend much of the TV news or talk shows. What could a person do with all that physical energy trapped inside his body? He paced around the house constantly like a caged animal, trying to figure out where he was and what he was supposed to do. On several occasions, he walked out of the house and got lost.

"Give me a chore," he would tell me, insistently and repetitively, clinging to me like a burr hanging in a dog's fur. There was nothing I could do to help him settle down, and none of the previous caregivers had had any luck either.

It was Charlie who came up with a solution to Clyde's restlessness by giving him some harmless tasks to pacify him, however temporarily. He handed Clyde a feather duster to "help" with dusting. He placed a basket full of old towels and worn T-shirts in front of him by the couch and asked Clyde to "help fold the laundry." He gave Clyde a broom to sweep the floor. Then Clyde got to fold the same old towels and T-shirts all over again. Charlie praised Clyde lavishly for "helping," and although I was sure that Clyde didn't deserve any praise for the result, he did deserve it for the effort. The former university president did the most minuscule chores with the same complete and earnest concentration he would have applied to a multimillion-dollar project for the university.

The chaos seemed to have receded now that Charlie and Ronnie were around. They both found ways to engage Clyde's attention and keep him occupied. Often, when I got home from work, I found the three of them talking while Charlie was preparing dinner. They discussed everything: the fabled history of the Lone Star State, tall tales from their childhood, American Indian legends, politics, war and the military, racial issues in America. There were differences among them, although they found plenty of common ground and listened to each other with restraint and respect. Clyde was a moderate conservative, whereas Charlie and Ronnie were moderate Democrats. Clyde was a Korean War veteran, and Charlie had grown up as an Army brat. Cherokee and Shawnee blood ran in Clyde's veins, Charlie's mother was a Cherokee, and both Charlie and Ronnie resented being considered "privileged white males." All three men had stories to tell about their respective mothers, the strong-minded women who had raised them and loved them unconditionally, earning their sons' endless affection and admiration in return.

I wasn't sure how many times the same stories got recycled. But who cares? After all, the memory-impaired lost his awareness of repetition, and the other two were content if repetition could preserve present harmony.

When conversation flagged and when domestic chores failed to pacify Clyde, it was time for a walk. Charlie took him to Williams Park, just steps away from home, where there were pleasant walking paths that meandered along manicured lawns and circled a small duck pond. They brought bread to feed the ducks.

On one trip to the park, out of the blue, Clyde started to imitate the quacking of the ducks.

"Clyde, can you show JoAnn how the ducks quack?" Charlie asked Clyde when they got home.

"Gua gua gua gua . . . gua gua gua gua." Clyde's imitation was better than I ever could have done even if I had practiced, and he did it with a child's zest. I laughed out loud. My laughter encouraged Clyde, and he started quacking some more.

"Gua gua gua gua . . . gua gua gua gua . . . gua gua gua gua."

He was pleased that he could still make his "Hon" laugh.

One day I came home after work and Charlie's report was: "We walked to the park seven times today."

Williams Park, University Park, Texas.

We all ate well in those days—Charlie could cook! To my Chinese taste buds, his cooking sometimes reflected the American tendency to ruin food by overseasoning it, leaving little room for appreciating the subtlety and complexity of flavors. Sugar-saturated cakes, salt-heavy soups, dressing-smothered salads, and the same "fry-it-up" approach to so many different foods, even cabbage, were just a few examples. He made meatloaf, which Clyde wouldn't eat because he didn't eat anything if he couldn't see what was in it. Then he proudly made salmon patties for us fish lovers. I politely tasted some, but Clyde declined. Neither of us cared for the taste of canned salmon. Once Charlie made a cake that had more icing than cake. The saying "the icing on the cake" implies that such a cake should be everyone's desire. But unlike the delicate, sophisticated icings on Shanghai cakes, Charlie's icing was just sugar and fat.[16]

On the other hand, we did like Charlie's spaghetti, chicken-fried steaks, and scalloped potatoes, although we wished they were less salty and greasy. We really liked his chili, with lots of meat and no beans. "Bean chili is for sissies, not for real Texans," Ronnie told me. And we loved Charlie's skillet cornbread made with bacon grease, his Southern-style overcooked green beans, and his turnip greens with ham hocks. There were black-eyed peas every New Year and peach cobblers when Texas peaches were in season.

We quickly learned to adapt to each other's food preferences and to compromise in our cooking styles. Charlie and Ronnie thought my Chinese cooking was delicious. Dumplings and fried rice were their favorites. I even got the two country boys to eat tofu with us and taught them how to season it so that it tasted like meat. When Charlie's nephew from a rural Texas town came to visit them in Dallas, they made a stir-fry dish with tofu and served it with rice.

"How did it go? What did your nephew and his wife think about the tofu dish?" I asked them, eager for a verdict.

"They loved it. They said the meat in the stir-fry was good, and both had seconds." They were delighted that their guests hadn't even realized they were eating tofu, not meat.

While Charlie and Ronnie were with us, I was able to get out and about with Clyde far more often than I would have if I had been trying to manage on my own. Alone, I could not get Clyde in and out of the car safely, make sure he kept his balance while walking, maneuver him in his wheelchair through difficult spaces, help him with his frequent latrine trips and occasional toileting mishaps, handle his constant confusion, and still have energy left to enjoy myself. A well spouse caring for an ill spouse with Alzheimer's encounters challenges every single moment. With Charlie and Ronnie sharing my burdens, I was able to enjoy many shining moments, those we consciously created with hope, humor, and heartfelt love for each other.

"The bird a nest, the spider a web, man friendship."[17] How wonderfully said by the English poet William Blake! The real home we build for ourselves is constructed of the people around us rather than brick and mortar.

For a couple of years, from summer 2005 to fall 2007, before Charlie had his first hospitalization and Clyde went to stay in an assisted-living facility, every Friday, Charlie and Ronnie took Clyde to our weekend home on Lake Ray Hubbard, some twenty miles outside Dallas. They picked up lunch for all of them at Dickey's Barbecue Pit en route and brought it to the lake house to eat. After lunch, Charlie cleaned the house and mowed the lawn while Ronnie watched Clyde until I got there in the evening after work. Charlie and Ronnie would come back to the lake house again on Saturday mornings to join Clyde and me for brunch on the patio by the lake. Charlie made scrambled eggs, bacon, and fresh biscuits.

Ah, those fluffy biscuits, hot out of the oven, moist inside with a golden crust!

One day while mowing the lawn of the lake house, Charlie found a turtle the size of a dinner plate casually strolling on the lawn. Charlie and Ronnie quickly picked it up and released it into the lake.

"You don't come back now," Charlie said to the turtle, "if you don't want to end up on JoAnn's dinner table. She is Chinese!"

For the mother goose who was hatching babies in the thick bed of reeds by the lake, we left bread that she devoured eagerly while keeping her distrustful eyes on us. Then one day, about three weeks later, Mama and babies were gone, leaving behind a pile of broken shells.

The Dallas Arboretum and Botanical Garden was a favorite place of ours during the warm seasons. In springtime, we sat under the fragrant cascading wisteria trellis outside DeGolyer House, overlooking the carpets of tulips, daffodils, and azaleas in a rainbow of brilliant colors. In summer, we spread a blanket on the lawn, laid out our picnic, and sang songs from the Flower Power era. Fall was the time to stroll among thousands of chrysanthemums and watch kids run around the pumpkin patch.

When the leaves were off the trees and the temperature had fallen, we took our walks inside NorthPark Center mall. As Christmas approached, we drove around the neighborhoods of University Park and Highland Park, admiring the spectacular holiday decorations. Together, we attended many concerts and holiday services in the Highland Park United Methodist Church at one corner of the SMU campus.

Sometime in early 2008, Clyde went out to eat with us for the last time. It was a Sunday. Charlie had recovered from the illness he had developed in the early fall of 2007 and was out of the hospital. We picked Clyde up at Monticello, an assisted-living facility where he had been staying since October 2007, after Charlie had been ill. Clyde's condition had progressed so far that we couldn't take him to regular restaurants anymore. He was in a wheelchair and had to be fed. If we didn't watch him every second, he would grab food off the plates, stab the table with the utensils, and spit nonstop everywhere. On that day, we decided to try the food court at NorthPark Center. We took a corner table away from the curious eyes of passersby. After lunch, I got us some ice cream, Clyde's all-time favorite treat. As Charlie pushed Clyde in the wheelchair, I held a giant ice-cream cone, doing my best to keep up so I could feed Clyde a few bites and eat some myself as we made our way through the mall. Ronnie, trailing behind, was holding an equally big ice-cream cone that he was supposed to share with Charlie, who had no spare hand to hold a cone himself. Of course, Ronnie conveniently forgot to make sure that Charlie got his share. In his other hand, Ronnie carried a bunch of napkins, busily wiping up the gobs of spit that Clyde was shooting out nonstop in all directions.

Quite an odd group in the eyes of observers, I was sure. But we just met people's probing eyes with smiles.

Ronnie, Charlie, Clyde, and the author at a Turtle Creek Chorale concert.

Every December around Christmastime, the Turtle Creek Chorale, one of the most celebrated all-male choruses in the country, performs a holiday concert. The chorus has more than 170 members, mostly gay men.[18] It is the premier opportunity in the Dallas gay community to see and be seen, an occasion for wearing the most elegant or innovative fashions. Knowing that this was a real treat for Charlie and Ronnie, I got tickets for us every year. It was the perfect way to celebrate Ronnie's birthday, which fell in the middle of December. The performance was always festive, beautiful, hilarious, and superbly entertaining. It was an evening we all looked forward to: dressing up, getting out of the house, enjoying some holiday cheer, and afterward, for sure, listening to Ronnie mercilessly making fun of *his* people's aesthetic senses, or lack of them, in clothing.

"Chuck, did you see him?" Ronnie said during one of the holiday shows, referring to a man Charlie had dated long ago. The gay community was relatively small, and they frequently ran into acquaintances or past lovers. "He sure isn't aging well—he shouldn't wear that toupee if he doesn't know how to put it on right."

Charlie ignored him, so Ronnie turned to me. "Chuck looks much better than him, doesn't he?"

Yes, I thought Charlie was a good-looking guy, but it was a mystery to me how Ronnie always knew just by looking that someone was wearing a hairpiece, a false mustache, fake lashes, or even fake boobs.

THE BIRD A NEST   57

On the evening of the Turtle Creek Chorale show in December 2006, Charlie was busy getting Clyde ready, taking him to the latrine, putting him in a tuxedo, and exchanging his slip-on house loafers for a pair of patent leather shoes that he had polished earlier that day.

Ronnie, meanwhile, was grooming himself and immediately got distressed.

"Chuck, my face looks terrible." He came out of the powder room, visibly upset. "Look at me! I can't go anywhere."

"What's wrong?" I asked.

"You look just fine, Ronnie." Charlie must have dealt with the problem a hundred times. He continued to work on Clyde and did not pay much attention to Ronnie.

"Here." Facing the light, he pointed to a lighter spot on his face close to his left temple that was hardly noticeable. "My color is off. What am I going to do? There is no way I can go to the chorale looking like this."

"What happened?" I asked. Charlie smiled, saying nothing, and continued to work Clyde's right foot into his shoe.

I was illiterate on the subject of cosmetics and had no idea that Ronnie's tanned skin was the result of painstakingly applied makeup. It was so out of the norm for me that I commented, "Ronnie, I think you are quite eccentric, queer, or is it peculiar?" Not sure of my word choice, I tried them all.

Ronnie forgot what was troubling him. He laughed so loud that he had to hold his belly, and so did Charlie.

"Chuck, did you hear what JoAnn just said? Am I a queer?" Ronnie said to Charlie, who was no longer squatting on his heels fiddling with Clyde's shoes, but sitting on the floor, bending over and laughing uncontrollably.

"Yes, I am." When Ronnie was able to catch his breath, he answered his own question, and then pointed to Charlie. "And so is he."

That was how I learned that *queer* as a noun refers to a gay man, in addition to what I had been taught in my English education in China, as an adjective meaning "strange."

At last we were all ready to go. Charlie and Ronnie were in black suits with freshly starched and pressed white shirts. Charlie had a yellow tie with blue stripes from Clyde's collection, Ronnie had a red one with black dots, and both wore shiny black leather shoes. Ronnie had recently lost a lot of weight and looked quite trim. Clyde was wearing a black necktie and his three-piece black tux, which Charlie had put on him with quite some effort. It still fit him perfectly after forty years. I was in a long royal purple velvet dress, white pearl earrings, a long white multistrand pearl necklace, a black satin handbag, and black leather heels that I had brought from China more than twenty years ago but that still looked brand new. We were confident that our group would turn heads, not only because people were often curious about how we were related, but also because each one of us looked mighty sharp that night.

We all got in my car, a pearl-white Cadillac SUV. Ronnie was driving, and Charlie sat by him in the front passenger seat. Clyde and I sat in the back. It was the very picture of a happy family.

Charlie turned his head, took a look at Ronnie, and said, "Good lord! Ronnie is drivin' a Cadillac again."

To which Ronnie responded, "Shut up, you queer!"

To which I recited Shakespeare, "'What's in a name? That which we call a rose by any other name would smell as sweet.'"[19]

The bird a nest.

Powder Room Etiquette.

Six

BATHROOM ETIQUETTE

Incoming traffic has the right of way.

—CLYDE WINGFIELD, an American

WINTER IN DALLAS IS NOT COLD COMPARED TO places like Chicago, where Clyde and I first met on a winter night in the late 1980s and where the cold season is an agonizing seven-month affair. But it was cold enough on this particular January night to make it tough to decide whether or not to leave the warmth of the goose down comforter and the coziness of the bed in order to use the bathroom. We set our bedroom temperature low, as we both preferred to sleep in cooler temperatures.

Perhaps it was Clyde's movements, or maybe it was my own urge to go in the middle of the night, but I woke up with a vague awareness that Clyde had just used the bathroom and returned to bed, and a clear sensation that my bladder was full.

To go or not to go? That was the question.

I grew up in China at a time when it was not uncommon for several families, each with multiple adults and children, to share one bathroom. Furthermore, public toilets were a rarity in those days. I had therefore learned to hold it well and long. Eventually, though, the urgency became imperative. Resolutely, I pulled myself out of bed, ran to the toilet, lowered my body, and relaxed my muscles to release the pressure that had been building up.

Ah, such a nice feeling! I felt the warm flow rushing freely as I slammed my rear down onto the toilet.

Just as fast, I jumped straight up as if I had sat on a hot fire.

"Oh, no!" I screamed. I would have cussed if I had known how.

I had not sat on a fire. I had plunked myself down onto the ice-cold rim of the toilet. The seat was up, and the rim was wet with what I knew it was, which had just struck my bare rear, which was still dripping from my warm flow, in the middle of a process I could not stop.

It was the most unpleasant sensation, completely appalling!

Standing there half naked, cold, wet, stinky, and in extreme agony, I wanted to scream, yell, cuss, and hit the culprit with a two-by-four to get his attention. Clyde had taught me a long time ago, "If you want to get someone's attention, hit him with a two-by-four." *Time to try it*!

Through the doorway, I could see the light from the bathroom gleaming dimly on the bed. Underneath the thick goose down duvet, the culprit's curled-up body rose and fell rhythmically with each breath, accompanied by the sound of snoring. Relaxed and content, apparently, he was undisturbed and untouched by my misery.

I took one long, slow, deep breath, and then another, trying to calm my fragile nerves.

Never mind, I said to myself with a willy-nilly head shake.

It took several more agonizingly cold, wet butts to finally reprogram my brain to accept that in my home, the warranty of a dry toilet with the seat securely down had expired. From the beginning of our cohabitation, Clyde and I had never had to debate whether the toilet seat should be left up or down, or at a forty-five degree angle. Mama Wingfield, Clyde's mother, had prudently taught her boys to put the toilet seat down before they were even old enough to ask that big "Why."

"I think it looks better to have the toilet seat down," Clyde told me. "And I think men should be considerate of women's needs."

I approved of such old-fashioned sentiments. "Manners are a sensitive awareness of the feelings of others. If you have that awareness, you have good manners," wrote Emily Post, America's best-known authority on manners and etiquette, "no matter what fork you use."[20] "Sensitive awareness of the feelings of others" has much importance in personal relationships. It can make or break the connection between lovers or among people in general. For all the years we had been together, Clyde and I had shared a belief and reciprocated the practice of being considerate of others' feelings. My husband had made me proud of his bathroom etiquette. Men, I knew, were not always aware of such mundane matters. I liked that in our home, toilet seats were put down. There was no dripping in front of the toilet, so I did not need to be afraid that my bare feet would step in urine and track it all over the house. Toothpaste residue and facial-hair clippings were rinsed off in the washbasin, wet towels were spread out to dry on the towel racks, and there was always a spare roll of toilet paper visible and within reach in the bathroom. Everything was in its duly designated place, not just for looks, but also out of thoughtfulness. Mama Wingfield's early discipline and Clyde's military training had made him a habitual creature of order, cleanliness, neatness, frugality, and most of all, consideration of others.

Signs of change started to appear about five years before Clyde was diagnosed with Alzheimer's disease. I began to notice repeated occurrences of lights left on, water left running, or drawers left open. Such sloppiness was a drastic departure from Clyde's usual orderliness and frugality, and I couldn't help but feel a little alarmed.

"You may have Alzheimer's," I joked, then added more seriously, "You better check with your doctor, at least to exclude the possibility."

He did. His doctor gave him a mini-scale mental health assessment. Clyde reported the findings when he came home.

"I am OK. I have some age-related memory loss, nothing more." It was a conclusion that both of us were happy to accept.

About two years after Clyde's formal diagnosis of Alzheimer's disease, I noticed one day that Clyde was pacing around the house, eyes wide open, peering left and right.

"Baby, what are you looking for?" By now, I knew that he had started having trouble recognizing familiar things.

"Honey, can you help me find a latrine?"

"What is a latrine?"

"Latrine. You know what that is. We have one here, I am sure."

"What is a latrine? I don't know the word."

"Honey. Come on, you know."

"No, I don't."

"Latrine, you know that. You know? I got to, to . . ."

Suddenly it dawned on me. "You mean a bathroom?"

"Yes, that's right. I am looking for a bathroom."

"Why did you call it a latrine? I have never heard that word." I took him by the hand and walked him to the powder room he had just passed before it was too late. The powder room was the only bathroom on the first floor where our kitchen, dining room, and family room were, and where we stayed during the day.

"In the military, we called it a latrine. I think it is a French word." Clyde was still my relentless teacher.

"Baby, can we please stick to English? English is hard enough for me. Let's not be fancy. Let's not start French now."

But from then on, *bathroom* disappeared forever from Clyde's world. It didn't exist at home or anywhere else. *Latrine* took its place for as long as Clyde could speak.

A World War II latrine. Photo from PBS, accessed on March 5, 2020, https://pbs.twimg.com/media/DBVjur9XgAAQM-E?format=jpg&name=900x900)

Things were happening in the latrine. The occasional incidents of lights left on or water left running now became frequent phenomena. I had already given up on the expectation that the toilet seat would be down and dry, and I often had to chase down the hand towel with my hands dripping wet. I needed to be prepared for a ghastly mess in the toilet staring back at me, because flushing was no longer in Clyde's consciousness. Worst of all, I often had to figure out how to get a roll of toilet paper gracefully while sitting on the toilet (no need to use imagination here).

"Baby, where did you leave the hand towel?"

"I don't know. I didn't take it."

"Baby, why do you keep taking the toilet paper away? It is so inconsiderate."

"I didn't do that. Did I do it?"

"Yes, you did."

"I don't remember."

"Baby, can you please not take the toilet paper out of the bathroom?"

"I am sorry. I won't do it again."

Mama Wingfield had undoubtedly taught her boys good Southern manners. Clyde was always polite and amicable. But if I thought my gentle guidance and patient perseverance would prevail in the face of these new challenges, I was wrong.

I mentioned earlier that someone once described Clyde this way: "Wingfield may be wrong, but never in doubt." Well, I was a Wingfield too. For a long time, I had no doubt I could restore a little order in the latrine if I only tried a little harder.

"Please remember to put the toilet seat down."

"Please don't take the toilet paper out."

"Please promise me that you will remember it."

"I promise," Clyde would say.

"Promise what? Let me hear it."

"Promise."

"Can you say you promise to remember not to take the toilet paper out of the bathroom?"

"You promise to remember."

In spite of my tireless efforts, Clyde's bathroom etiquette did not get better; it got worse. One day, while I sat on the toilet staring in dismay at the empty toilet paper holder, a brilliant idea came to me. Why not post a sign in the latrine just like those we all see in women's public restrooms: NO SANITARY NAPKINS IN THE TOILET? I was sure that Clyde had seen something like that in men's restrooms . . . well, maybe not about sanitary napkins.

Don't we all follow such instructions? I do.

I told Clyde that I was going to post a sign in the latrine reminding *us* about the etiquette. He supported the idea eagerly and wanted to help wholeheartedly.

"Hon, read to me what you've written. Let me help you."

I read what I had come up with earlier while sitting on the toilet waiting for him to deliver some toilet paper (he couldn't follow my directions to the toilet paper supply, but I was able to retrieve some gently used tissues from the hoard in his pocket).

He listened attentively. When I had finished, he paused for a while, then asked, "Honey, could you repeat that?"

I did, one sentence at a time, and waited for him to comprehend and respond.

"Can you think of anything else we should include?" I asked.

"Read that sentence again." He pointed his fingers in the air, as if some words were written somewhere there.

I started to repeat the entire passage again, and paused at the sentence that read, "Thou shall leave the wastes to appropriate place."

"Should I use 'wastes' or 'waste'?" I prompted. Singular and plural in the English language often confused me.

"Waste, waste . . ." He was mumbling, thinking hard. "You have it right."

"Then I should use 'places' instead of 'place'"?

He approved that change. Thus, I had, "Thou shall leave wastes to appropriate places." I realized we both had been wrong only after a friend pointed out to me years later that both words should have been in the singular form.

Oh, well.

Thus the "Powder Room Etiquette" was born, the brainchild of the marriage of our two brilliant minds. I used an old-fashioned font called

Edwardian Script that had elegant cursive strokes. I surrounded the text with a Victorian-style border of a curling leafy vine to echo the text and printed the passage in color, black for the text and sage green for the border, on a piece of cream paper. Finally, I put the sign in a black-and-brown wooden frame and hung it in the powder room on the wall facing the toilet, right where one's eyes had direct contact with it while sitting squarely on the seat.

It read like this:

Powder Room Etiquette
Thou shall use the room to meditate;
Thou shall not leave the seat up;
Thou shall flush after using;
Thou shall not take the towel out;
Thou shall leave the wastes to appropriate places;
Thou shall respect all functions of this room.

As planned, the sign did not go unnoticed. My guests came out of the powder room smiling and complimented me on how thoughtful the sign was. The maddening disorder in the latrine, however, not only failed to disappear; it grew worse. Clyde's proper Southern manners and praiseworthy etiquette became a distant memory. Still, this memory really helped me, the well spouse, to keep things in perspective amid the chaos and desolation of our remaining years together.

The communal latrine at Ephesus (first-century CE).

At a dance dinner in Maggiano's Little Italy restaurant, Dallas, 2006.

Seven

THE LAST DANCE

Fairies, come take me out of this dull world,
for I would ride with you upon the wind, . . .
and dance upon the mountains like a flame.

—W. B. YEATS, The Land of Heart's Desire

BOTH OF THEM LIKED DANCING; NEITHER OF THEM was very good. Some foxtrot, some jitterbug, a little swing, and a lot of improvising, all blended together—they danced as they pleased, to the beat of whatever music was playing. They didn't care about looking good or being technically precise, nor did anyone else. They just loved the feeling of their bodies being in sync and their spirits in harmony.

Over the years, their steps swirled together smoothly, or not so smoothly after her husband's Alzheimer's disease progressed, across all kinds of floors: the shiny white tile floors of the giant living room in their Ranchita home, just the two of them alone; the grassy lawn outside the house, with her mom and dad, visiting from Shanghai, watching and smiling; the gritty cement walkway under the fragrant cascading wisteria in the Dallas Arboretum, with Charlie and Ronnie; the polished floor of the banquet room in Maggiano's Little Italy, a restaurant in NorthPark Center mall, with friends and the singing of a Frank Sinatra impersonator; on the dance floor of the legendary Arlington Hotel in Hot Springs, Arkansas, tracing the steps of the hotel's famous guests, Franklin D. Roosevelt, Harry Truman, George H. W. Bush, Bill Clinton, Babe Ruth, Tony Bennett, and Barbra Streisand, as well as the most infamous guest, Al Capone;[21] on the floating deck of a small country diner on Lake Ray Hubbard in Rowlett, Texas, with Clyde's daughter and his grandchildren, to the melancholy tunes of a local country-western band; on the crowded dance floor of the opulent *Queen Mary 2*, drifting over the Mediterranean Sea.

Over the years of their life together, she had learned his moves, and he hers.

Slowly and sadly, as Clyde's mind deteriorated, he started to forget their moves, his and hers. But she, the well spouse, did not.

Four years after Clyde's Alzheimer's diagnosis, in 2006, an interesting event transpired about our solar system. Pluto was demoted by the International Astronomical Union (IAU) from a planet to a dwarf planet for not having sufficient mass to clear "*its neighboring region of other objects*," one of the IAU's three criteria necessary for classification as a planet.[22] It became a lonely dwarf planet in the solar system, with the other eight full-fledged planets leaving it out in a series of memes. If the fate of the mighty Pluto could be so uncertain, what of the fate of ordinary people on this planet?

It was an ordinary summer day. She came home from work and relieved Charlie of his duties. After dinner was over and chores were done, she sat down on the couch, Clyde by her side. She turned on the TV, hoping to kill some time with mindless entertainment. She chatted a little with Clyde, mostly the kind of inconsequential conversation that she used to engage Clyde's attention, to keep him here.

"Clyde, did you and Charlie go feed the ducks today?"

Clyde looked at her, thinking, but nothing came to his mind. He was not able to answer the question that required recall, however simple it was.

"Baby, can you do a duck quacking?"

"Qua, qua, qua." That he was able to do, effortlessly.

She laughed and rewarded him with a kiss. Science tells us that when people cuddle, cozy up, or snag a good hug with each other, their brains release oxytocin, known as the "love" or "cuddle" hormone, which can lower stress and make them feel closer. Even petting a dog or cat can boost one's mood. Maybe that was why she had always loved their physical connection and still did, even though her husband had lost a great deal of his awareness and sometimes seemed to be off in a world of his own. She loved necking and cuddling with him, as if she had never grown out of her adolescence desires, stroking his hair, feeling his cheeks, neck, shoulders, torso, and limbs, aware of the texture of his bones, flesh, skin, and his scent and warmth. In her native country, during her younger years, any open display of affection between people of the opposite sex was considered unconventional, uncommon, and inappropriate, and was discouraged.

"Bourgeois sentimentality," people sneered.

"Not proper," mothers admonished.

Here in the US, freedom of expression was her right, and the "no-touch" ban was lifted for her. She could shower her husband with affection wherever, whenever, and however she liked—embracing, kissing, stroking his face, holding his hand, clinging to his arms, clasping his shoulder, wrapping her arm around his waist. Suppressed desire has a way of resurfacing more fiercely. She often wondered if her desire to touch her husband all the time was a way of making up for her touch-deprived earlier life in China.

Besides, Clyde relished his wife's attention. He encouraged it and reciprocated with equal, if not greater, affection, making her feel that she could finally be herself, displaying her "bourgeois sentimentality" as much as she wanted.

Now that Clyde's ability to use language had largely faded, smooching played a more significant role in their communication. It was her way of saying to him, Hi, Baby. I am here. Be here with me. I love you.

Clyde understood her message. He responded to her touch in kind, and sometimes his responses were even verbal: "I love you, Hon," he said.

In the middle of the mindless TV watching, Clyde's tangled mind wandered.

"Hon, let's go home. Are you ready?"

"Wait a little longer." She had seen this coming, so she dawdled along and resorted to Tactic One: Delaying Action. "Clyde, Baby, I want to finish watching this program with you."

"OK, no rush." His patience with her was endless. But in less than two minutes, he stood up and said, "Hon, let's go home. I am ready."

"Sit down with me. I love to sit with you. You always feel so good to me." She held his hand and sat him down by her on the couch again. She hooked her arms around him and laid her head on his shoulder to keep him there. "I am so happy we are together like this." This was her Tactic Two: Coaxing and Sugaring. All men liked their ego to be cajoled. Clyde might be ill, but he was still a man. "The show's almost over. We will go soon." She had no intention of going anywhere but was in no way ashamed of her lie. They *were* home.

"OK, very soon." He trusted her and placed one of his arms on her back, gently patting her as if she were a child. That almost made her purr.

If Clyde gets too restless, then I will take him to the grocery store, she thought. *We will get a couple of grapefruit and some vanilla ice cream.* This would be Tactic Three: Diverting Attention. She hoped that a trip to the store would make Clyde forget that elusive home in la-la land. His favorite fruit and ice cream might comfort his shattered mind as well as her own fatigued psyche.

At last it was time to get ready for bed. She gave Clyde his last medicine for the day, helped him brush his teeth, wash, and undress, and got him to lie down between the soft, finely woven cotton sheets, the only kind that could soothe Clyde's sensitive skin and calm his constant stirring. She placed a plastic basin by the bed and a mat right where Clyde's feet would touch the floor when he got out of bed. In Clyde's vintage, he now needed to use the bathroom several times a night, but he was no longer aware of where he was supposed to pee, so he would stand by the bed and let himself go. She would have only a few seconds to catch it.

I feel like a nursing mother again, she sighed to herself, her heart filled with maternal love for her husband, whose once brilliant mind had now reverted to the level of an infant's.

She finally lay down next to her husband. Clyde was sleeping on his back with his eyes shut. Tenderly, she kissed his closed eyes, teased his eyelashes with her lips, smoothed his fine silky hair off his forehead, and drew a little breath, inhaling his scent, the pleasant and comforting smell that defined him for her. Like an animal, she was very sensitive to smell. The familiar scent of her loved ones reassured her that they were there, close to her.

She read in bed for a little while. It was her lifelong habit. After a few palpitating chapters of Dan Brown's *The Da Vinci Code*—mysteries were her favorite nighttime escape—and a few calming pages of a gardening catalog—she loved gardening, watching life thriving—she switched off the light. Outside in the darkness, distant thunder rumbled. Turning to face the wall, she nudged Clyde a little to get her body settled, feeling the touch of their flesh against each other, warm and innocent; they always slept naked. She was relaxed and began to drift off. . .

In this trancelike state, she felt a disturbance from the other side of the bed. In an instant, all her sensors returned to a highly alert point.

Is Clyde getting up?

Holding her breath, she waited for a second, anticipating Clyde's next movement, preparing to eject herself out of bed. If she were only a second too late, Clyde would have gotten up before she could and would have peed on the floor. Then she would need to clean up the mess in the middle of the night. It had already happened several times, and she did not think it was a pleasant prospect.

But Clyde didn't try to get up. Instead, he turned toward her back and nestled his body against hers. His warm breath began to tickle the back of her neck. *That feels good!* Like a dog, she wiggled her body to let go of the tension and edged it over to spoon with him, something they did often and well. Now they had formed a perfect spoon. With neither of them over- or underweight, and their compatible body size and mass, their bodies made for a perfect fit. When curled against each other, they were like two layered cabbage leaves from the same head of the cabbage, one huddled with the other, with hardly any gap between them.

Clyde continued to stir. Uncertainly, his arms reached over to touch her; his face rubbed her back very lightly, and he mumbled, "Hon, you, you . . ." His hand traveled across the curves of her waist, her hip, her belly, and her legs, moving aimlessly. She sensed some clumsy activity from the lower part of his body, as if he were in search of something, something. . . .

All of a sudden, she recognized that move and she understood his quest. Her heart tightened. She felt a twitch inside; at the same time, her eyes grew warm and moist. That something her husband was searching for was as original as the beginning of creation, and as ancient as Adam and Eve. Instinctively, he was in search of life's perpetuation, and he was lost. He had lost the ability so fundamental to a man, so deeply coded in his being, so indispensable to the survival of the human race, an ability he had once mastered so deftly.

For her, the mating ritual had become like a pair of old shoes, not entirely cast away but only occasionally remembered, and she was often too tired, too stressed, too occupied with being the spousal caregiver, or too uncertain about his physical condition to pursue it. It was a cruel and painful revelation that the dreadful Alzheimer's disease had robbed him of the capability to be a man, and taken from both of them something so deeply intimate, so precious, so essential in defining their relationship, and there was nothing she could do to stop it.

Silently, she said to him, *Let me take you home, Baby, let me take you home.*

She took his right hand in hers, running it slowly across the gentle peaks and valleys of her body, drifting it back and forth on her rounded belly, gliding it up her hip and down over her indented waist, letting it trace and linger in circles on her modest breasts. It was a familiar yet strange sensation, lustless yet sensual, and beyond mere pleasure. It was almost spiritual. She felt no excitement, no anticipation, only a great deal of sorrow.

Baby, do you remember all this?

She remembered their first time and many times after. As if they were dancing to the processions of a symphonic performance, the beginning was often an *adagio*, an introduction in which they danced slowly, timidly, and tentatively, with heart-aching tenderness. Then came the *scherzo*, when their dance became lighthearted and playful and their yearning grew stronger. This led into the *allegro*, in which the dance grew faster and bolder, more upbeat, more passionate, and almost frenzied. Suddenly, the *finale* arrived. The proverbial bang—fireworks exploded, stars collided, and heaven opened its doors. And then the performance came to an abrupt end.

But don't expect an encore or even a curtain call. All the lights went out.

But when was the last time we made love? Three months ago? Six? Or was it a year? She searched her memory, finding nothing.

Without turning her body over to face him, she reached back to touch him. Her hand slid over his body, first his firm outer thigh, then the sensitive inside, then his lower back, flat and accessible. She savored the texture of his skin, soft, smooth, and warm, and she wondered if Clyde still relished the touch of her "expressive hands," as he had once called them.

She placed her hand on his buttock, feeling its fleshiness and tenderness. *Why do they call it "cheek" in English?* she remembered asking Clyde. It was still funny to her. She pressed his buttock closer to her and felt his carnal desire grow stronger.

As if hearing his heart murmuring, she heard him saying to her: *Hon, lead me. Take me home.*

She remembered that when they first started to dance together, anytime her movements got ahead of his, Clyde would say to her, "Hon, I cannot dance being led." He would lose track of his steps, and they would have to stop and realign. Clyde couldn't follow. Clyde had to lead.

What a reversal of roles! Now I must lead, and Baby, you will follow.

With her back still turned toward him, she pushed herself into him, deeper, deeper, until there was no distance between them, until they were almost just one body. She wanted him in her, one more time. She wanted to squeeze him, hold him there, and not let him go. She wanted to do to him everything he had ever desired, giving him every bit of herself and devouring every bit of him. She wanted Clyde to do exactly the same to her. She wanted the ache and the certainty the ache would bring. She wanted him to take her boiling body and burning soul, all of it. She wanted to feel his weight on top of her, making her feel both vulnerable and secure.

One more time, just once more.

But it was not going to happen. It was *never* going to happen! No more partnership, no more reciprocation. She was now in charge, and she must take both of them home on her own.

With that thought, she rolled Clyde over and got on top of him.

She started to move, first slowly and then more vigorously, until her breath became fast and labored. Sweat emerged from her forehead, her armpits, and her chest. She posted atop him like an equestrienne, hooking her knees outside his legs, and rode him as if he were her horse. He was her horse! She took his hands to touch her breasts and buttocks, to wake up his senses to her womanhood.

Baby, do you feel my body? Do you register me? Her soul cried out to him. Answering her was the thunder in the distance. Rain was coming.

She wanted Clyde to take pleasure in her. She knew that he did. It was a simple pleasure, and it didn't require his understanding. She pondered the nature of human sexuality. *How could something so simple be so wonderful, so reliably the same for millions of years? How cruel to be deprived of such essential joy.* At some point, she opened her eyes and saw Clyde watching her. Was he measuring her? Could he feel her emotions? Did he understand that she was making love to him? *What does it matter?* She shook her head, as if shaking off cobwebs tangling it, and bent down to kiss her husband's eyes.

Outside, in the darkness, the thunder roared closer. Lightning penetrated the pea-green silk curtains embroidered with tiny white flowers and flared, flashing violently over her flesh with sharp blows. Suddenly she felt furious, and she felt the need to wreak vengeance on the sorrow she had been storing up inside herself. Her eyes sparked with anger, her movements grew forceful, and she was filled with rage and vigor.

Damned Alzheimer's disease!

All at once, desire that had lain dormant, buried under the mundane tasks of caregiving, the stress of work, and the weight of emotional pain, awakened like fire meeting dry grass. She moved with such intense force and speed that she was panting. She felt her husband, her precious love, responding to her: he was growing mighty, manly, solid, and resilient. Extreme pleasure pulsed through her body in every direction. Powerful passion, maddening passion swept over her. Her emotions were a complex and perplexing confusion: grief, exhilaration, tenderness, ferocity, and a frenzied sense of possession. She embraced him, kissed him, wept over him, and at the same time, shook him so hard, as if she wanted him to wake up from the horrendous dream that had fogged his mind, and to recognize her without a shred of doubt. She wanted this moment to be deeply imprinted on his consciousness.

Rain and clouds.

As she drove herself harder onto him, moaning with pleasure, the immensely big universe receded as their own private universe, exclusively theirs, expanded to fill all space. The rain was pouring down in torrents now, banging loudly on the windows. *Rain and clouds, clouds and rain,* one could no longer tell which was which.[23] Their bodies fused into one; there was no his or hers. Their souls united, not his and hers, but one. There was no separation between living and dying—there *is* no separation between living and dying. We are all living, and we are all dying.

People are not able to choose their own birth and, for the most part, not able to choose their own death, she thought, *but I will choose how to love and how to live, regardless of what's happening in my life. That is exactly what I will do!*

She searched for his soul, for a sign of recognition and the assurance of his love. She felt a flicker of it, or did she? But it was hard to catch, it was hard to be certain, and it slipped away into obscurity just as quickly as it sparkled in the darkness, before she could catch it, before she could be certain.

Underneath her, Clyde's body lifted and heaved. He responded to her frenzied movements, perhaps driven by the calling of a mysteriously immortal code planted deep in his mortal being. His eyes were shut, his mouth faintly twitching. She spun her hips and felt him inside her, mighty, muscular, and manly.

Baby, come, come home with me!

As she slid herself up and down, left and right, forward and back, they both fell into their own urgent rhythms and overlapping disturbances, like separate waves from the same storm, first dampening, then amplifying one after another. She felt the inexorability of the crescendo toward climax begin. She cried out loud, shaking and gasping for breath. Beads of sweat joined each other to form strands, then little streams, running down her face, neck, and breasts, dripping onto Clyde. With her body still bouncing strongly and rapidly, she felt Clyde's torso and limbs stiffen under her as he let out a cry, one she knew well. She imagined his useless seeds spurting out—millions of potential lives, all with equal opportunity, as none of them would have any hope to be somebody, someday.

Clyde started to dissolve. She collapsed on top of him, spent. In some distant corner of her mind, the beautiful Norwegian singer Sissel Kyrkjebø was singing tenderly:

> Going home, going home
> I'm just going home
> Quiet-like, some still day
> I'm just going home
>
> It's not far, just close by
> Through an open door
> Work all done, care laid by
> Going to fear no more[24]

She rolled off her husband and folded herself toward him. Their bodies rested in heavy stillness on the bed. Snuggling under his left arm, she rested her head on Clyde's shoulder and entwined her limbs with his. Quietly, she let the tears stream down from the corners of her eyes, let them flow between her face and Clyde's shoulder and continue down to soak the pillow. The storm outside had retreated, and the rain had stopped. Through the curtains, a delicate glow streamed in from the streetlight.

Clyde moved his face to touch hers and took a kiss from her. She set her head a little further back on his shoulder, watching his silhouette. In the low light, she could see his closed eyes, but not the lashes she adored. She could make out his prominent nose, the "Indian chief nose," as she often teased, referring to his American Indian ancestry; and his resolute lips. His face was serene, as dear as ever.

Baby, are you happy? Do you feel loved? Do you love me? She wished she could know his thoughts now.

In her heart, she mourned. She knew this was their last dance. The fire was dwindling, the stars descending. Like two planets in the universe, their paths met, and their journeys joined. Now that same mysterious and mighty force that had brought them together and blessed them with so much happiness was taking him away from her. Clyde, her darling husband, her precious love, was orbiting away from her, irreversibly and irrevocably, farther and farther, like a fading star. Soon he would be out of her reach, out of anyone's reach.

Farewell, my love.

In Dallas Arboretum, 2008.

Kennebunkport, Maine, 2006.

Eight

TRAVEL THE WORLD
AND THE SEVEN SEAS

*Only those who will risk going too far can possibly
find out how far one can go.*

—T. S. ELIOT, preface to Transit of Venus by Harry Crosby

S OUTHAMPTON, AUGUST 2005. The ship slid gently out of the port
toward the busy waters of the English Channel, bound for the warm
waters of the Mediterranean. Clyde and I stood on the deck of this
majestic lady, the RMS *Queen Mary 2*, eagerly waving at people on shore
who were absolute strangers to us. As the ship moved gracefully into open
water, the sea and sky appeared to merge into one body of profoundly
unfathomable blue. While the people on shore slowly receded from view,
around us on board, bubbly champagne flowed freely, and salty lilting
reggae music followed in our wake.

Only a few moments before, en route to the port, we had passed the
modest landmark showing where some 385 years ago, in September 1620,
the Mayflower had left England to sail for America. It seemed surreal
to me to be here, on the *Queen Mary 2*, which came from the same line

of ships as the legendary but ill-fated RMS Titanic. As I was looking forward to visiting not just one or two or even three, but a staggering seven of the world's most beautiful countries with Clyde, starting there in England and going on to Portugal, Spain, France, Italy, Vatican City, and Monaco, I sighed deeply and squeezed his arm:

"Baby, I have dreamed of this day many times. We have made it happen."

The plan had been that Clyde and I were going to travel the world after I retired, at some time in the unknown future.

"I want to go to Italy first. I want to see Renaissance art," I told Clyde whenever I started daydreaming about our future travels.

"Whenever you are ready, I will be happy to show you what I know." Having been to Italy a couple of times, including one stay in the 1980s that had lasted a few months while he was co-organizing a symposium with Italian scholars in Rome, Clyde might be able to chaperone me around the Eternal City almost as well as Joe Bradley had chaperoned Princess Ann in the movie *Roman Holiday*.

Wouldn't that be swell!

"I also want to go to Greece, to talk to the great sages of Western civilization, Plato especially."

"Why Plato?"

"Because I want him to enlighten me about the Vulgar Eros and the Divine Eros," I joked, referring to the so-called sensual love and Platonic love.

"You don't have to go to Greece to be enlightened. You can go to the library." Clyde's tendency to meet my obvious nonsense with utter seriousness never ceased to amuse me.

"And India," I dreamed on. "To see the sunrise on the River Ganges."

"People get sick there. You must be very careful." He sounded as if I were leaving for India the next morning. Having gotten sick several times on international trips, he was big on the germ theory.

"And Egypt, too. I am fascinated with all ancient civilizations."

"But you grew up in one of the world's oldest civilizations." He might not have been as enthusiastic about traveling the world as I was, but he always assured me, "Hon, we will go when you are ready."

At the time, I was at the prime of my creativity and productivity. I loved and was devoted to my career, and retirement was nowhere near. But now that Clyde had Alzheimer's, his condition was unpredictable, and his traveling days were numbered. It was now or never. So when my sister Hai invited me to sail with her and her husband on the *Queen Mary 2*, whose maiden voyage had occurred just one year before, I eagerly accepted. At the time, the *QM2*, the flagship of the Cunard Line, was the biggest, newest, and most luxurious of all cruise ships.

We had talked about cruising before Clyde became ill, but he had not been enthusiastic. He thought *we* would feel too confined.

"Hon, I have cruised before, and I know what it's like. I don't think you would enjoy it." He had a tendency of projecting his likes and dislikes onto me.

Clyde was referring to a voyage he had taken at the end of the Korean War, when he was a young Air Force lieutenant. He was put in charge of about three hundred enlisted men on board a ship (Perhaps it was the USS *Walker*, when it sailed from San Diego, USA, to Okinawa, Japan?).[25] On the monthlong journey across the Pacific Ocean, most of his men got seasick, vomiting and moaning all over the ship. It was not a pretty picture. It was not a pleasant journey.

I had reasoned with him unsuccessfully in the past that those old-time military vessels were no match for the modern-day floating cities, and that a military tour of duty was no comparison to a luxurious pleasure cruise. Now, using the argument that we could travel to seven countries, with a dozen ports of call, all the while staying in the same room and never having to pack or unpack (changing rooms was very confusing for him now, and packing was strictly my responsibility), I was able to persuade him to "travel the world and seven seas" with me. I knew it would be challenging to travel with someone who had dementia, but, as a woman who had survived the "Red Storms" of the Cultural Revolution and thirteen years of sandstorms in the Gobi Desert of Inner Mongolia, I could not be easily intimidated. Clyde's Alzheimer's had cast a distinct shadow of death over our lives, which made making the most out of living with Clyde all the more imperative. *Sein-zum-Tode*, "being-toward-death," as the German philosopher Martin Heidegger told us, is a fundamental part of being human.[26] Making memories in the limited, uncertain time we had ahead of us became an unwavering priority of mine.

Other than the four of us, our group included two other couples who were friends with Hai and her husband. We dined together at a designated table. At the end of dinner on the first night, after dessert had been served, Clyde said to me discreetly, "Hon, I want to treat all your friends. Can you help me?"

Everyone but Clyde knew that all meals were included, even if we were not on a military voyage. Nevertheless, I conveyed the message to the group, with a wink. We were all a little amused; the others knew he had Alzheimer's disease. With good humor, they thanked Clyde for the dinner he hadn't paid for.

After dinner, we all went to the shows. After the shows, we all went to the dance hall, where live music was playing. I quickly discovered that the former Air Force officer, who had drunk whiskey, smoked cigars, and danced the night away effortlessly in the officer's clubs, no longer made his swirls as smoothly around the dance floor, and the formerly eloquent, versatile conversationalist was having trouble following our conversations. When I accepted an invitation to dance, or conversed with others, Clyde was left to sit alone, awkwardly. When he did join in, everyone else was left out, equally awkwardly, because it was hard to make sense of what he said. Often people are at a loss as to how to socialize with someone who has dementia, so they avoid it altogether.

Sensing, or imagining, that we were creating uneasiness in the group, I asked Clyde to take a walk with me on deck.

"But Hon, I want to stay here. I like it here." He hadn't picked up on my discomfort.

My heart tightened. I felt like the mother of a child with disabilities who, innocent and harmless, has no awareness of his or her limitations; the mother is all too aware and must shield her child from the reality, the naked, cruel reality.

Baby, we no longer belong here.

"I feel nauseated," I said. "I shouldn't have had that piña colada. Alcohol always gives me a headache. But it tasted so good—I forgot that I couldn't drink. I need some fresh air."

I took his hand, and out we walked onto the deck. Not a flicker of light was visible on the horizon. Darkness surrounded us, except for our formidable floating city, with its towering eighteen decks, which illuminated the boundless darkness like a giant in gleaming armor. I took a few deep breaths of the warm, moist Mediterranean air, expelling a little bit of my grief each time I exhaled.

Clyde had already forgotten the packed dance hall with its passionate music. Halfway through a turn around the deck, we were distracted by the sound of a piano playing in one of the lounges. We walked inside and sat down at one of the tables. A man was singing as he played the piano. After listening to a few tunes, we joined a game of "Guess That Tune." Each table was given a number and a scorecard. Ours was table eight, a lucky number for Chinese people, as the pronunciation for eight (ba八) closely resembles that of "prosper" or "flourish" (fa发) in Chinese.

"Clyde, you are on your own," I told him. "I won't be of any help."

The pianist struck a few keys. Quickly, someone shouted out a song title, guessing it right. They got a star to stick on their scorecard. Clyde smiled and said that he was going to guess the same but was just one beat too slow. Another few notes sounded, and Clyde called out the name of the song. Yes! He got it! Another series of notes—Clyde called out and got it right again! Someone at table two got the next one. As the game went on, more stars went to tables eight and two than to any other tables.

Then came another few notes, and everyone went quiet. People looked at each other and shook their heads. Our neighbors at table two looked at us, and I looked at Clyde, who shook his head slightly. Darn! No one got that one.

Finally, it was time to tally up the stars. First place went to table two, and table eight was a close second, just one star short.

"Clyde, if you had had a partner who could help, you'd be in first place." I was sure of that because table two had four people. I gave him a big hug. He was still my hero.

Clyde smiled. "I was lucky." He was still a humble man.

I carefully studied the daily excursions and chose the ones that would work best for us: those that were interesting (to me, at least) but that required only a moderate time commitment and that were less demanding physically and cognitively. Clyde was happy for me to take advantage of his dependency.

"Honey, you choose for us. You know what we like."

Some days, he was not in the most cooperative mood.

"I don't want to climb the rock." I had told him that we were going to the Rock of Monaco that day. He correctly associated "rock" with "climbing," which intimidated him.

"No, not that type of rock." I tried to explain, but his brain was insisting on the linkage between "rock" and "climbing."

"I don't want to get sweaty. I will come down with pneumonia." He often came up with excuses to avoid doing things that seemed daunting. "You know I am prone to pneumonia." He was remembering that he had had pneumonia as a baby and had almost died from it.

"Baby, you don't have to go. You stay on the ship. I will go by myself." Calling his bluff was one of my weapons for a while, and it was quite effective most of the time. "But what are you going to do while I am gone?"

The choice was obvious to him. Being without me was definitely more intimidating than the rock. So he came along, didn't have to climb anything, and enjoyed every step with me.

For the rest of the trip, with some sadness, I avoided joining my sister and her gang for activities so that we would not slow them down. When Clyde was setting off for Japan in the Air Force, his father gave him two pieces of advice: "Never volunteer" and "Never miss an opportunity." We never missed an opportunity to use the restrooms. Every place we went, the first and last task was getting Clyde to a restroom, because men of Clyde's vintage have their particular attachment to restrooms, and the next opportunity might come too late. We always planned extra time for logistics such as getting on and off the tour bus, eating, getting back to the ship, and taking restroom breaks, which meant cutting down on time for sightseeing activities. Slowing down was not easy for me—I was used to a fast and furious pace and was thirsty to see more and do it all—but as a well spouse, I really had to accept limitations like these.

As the others in the group kept dashing off for the most exciting adventures and beckoning to us to come along, Hai looked at me sympathetically, saying nothing. I knew she understood my dilemma.

"No, you guys go ahead." I waved at them with a smile. But inside, I felt like a bird with broken wings, no longer able to fly high and free. I looked at Clyde, my dear, clueless husband, and squeezed his hand to feel his presence. *Baby, I am grateful that we are together.* Savoring the moment at hand made it easier for me to accept our constraints. Someday in the foreseeable future, even this would be lost.

One day, we went on a morning excursion and returned to the ship by noon. After lunch, it was just one o'clock and the order to return to the ship would not come until five. We had the entire afternoon free. I wanted to get off the ship and take a walk in the picturesque seaside town lined with tantalizing bakeries and charming little shops.

"Baby, let's go on shore." I was always ready for some action.

"Hon, I am tired. I don't want to go out again."

"But we have the whole afternoon. What would we do instead?"

"I am going to take a nap. I am exhausted." His eyes looked heavy, as if he hadn't slept well in the night, but I knew he did, and I was concerned that a nap would ruin his sleep in the night, and mine too.

"Come on, you will feel better once we get out." I believed in pushing limits, mine or his or anyone else's, and I coaxed him a little. "I promise we won't walk too much."

"I really don't want to go."

"OK, then I will go. You can stay." I tested my weapon again, feeling confident that he wouldn't want to be left without me, ever!

"You can go, Hon. I just need to rest a bit." He started to lie down on the bed.

Oops, weapon failure! What could I do? My body was bubbling with energy seeking release, and my spirit was full of curiosity, craving all the wonders of life and yearning to experience every corner of the world. This suppressed desire had grown so strong that it was ready to explode.

I want to go! I don't want to stay. I want to be free!

My heart, bursting with longing, screamed in frustration and fought with my rational mind, which answered with unshakable power: *But you love him. He is dependent on you. This is your fate.*

Knowing that I would never leave Clyde unattended, I crawled into the bed, lay down next to him, and turned my back against him. Clyde turned over to spoon with me, as was our habit. With my body contoured along his, my face away from him, and my spirit broken, I wept quietly for a long time as he slept undisturbed. Flowing out with my tears came not only grief, but also defeat, surrender, and self-pity.

"Frailty, thy name is woman." Shakespeare came mocking.

That evening, we didn't go to the dining room to have dinner with the gang. I didn't want the others to see my puffy red eyes.

Broken-winged I might have been, but I had never wanted to let our limitations stop us from going places for as long as we could. We visited places and people connected with Clyde's early life, with the goal of reinforcing memories for him and creating new ones for me. Soon after his diagnosis, we took a road trip to Curtis, Arkansas, where his sister Georgianna showed me the house where Clyde was born and the mulberry tree whose berries he had picked as a little boy. We drove around the campus of Henderson State University, where he had started before transferring to East Texas State College (now part of Texas A&M). We visited a close friend of his from childhood, who was a little startled that during lunch, Clyde chewed on his teabag, thinking it was some kind of food, before I stopped him. The friend didn't ask, and I didn't tell.

We went to Miami and Fort Lauderdale often to see Clyde's daughter, Joy, and her family. One of the Florida trips also took us to Key West, where we visited Harry Truman's Little White House and the house of Ernest Hemingway, who advised travelers, "Never go on trips with anyone you do not love."[27] Wise advice! My travel companion had lost a few cards, but he was still my beloved. In Kansas City, Missouri, we attended Clyde's son William's graduation ceremony when he received his master's degree in educational leadership. Will had decided to go to the ceremony for his father's sake—again, to create memories. On that trip, we visited Truman's

Presidential Library & Museum and stopped in Hannibal, Missouri, to see the boyhood home of Mark Twain, who famously said, "It's not the size of the dog in the fight; it's the size of the fight in the dog."[28]

The size of the fight in me was formidable. I pushed on, dealing along the way with Clyde's confusion, his diminished ability to function, his difficulty in using the latrine, and his messy eating. I was doggedly determined to create what memories we could, make the best of a bad situation, live as fully as possible, and have no regrets.

On the island of Barbados, we saw the castle of the buccaneer Sam Lord, which Clyde had visited before. His stories about Sam had incited my fascination ever since. In Savannah, Georgia, we toured historic antebellum homes preserved by James Arthur Williams, whose sensational murder trials formed the basis for John Berendt's 1994 account, *Midnight in the Garden of Good and Evil*; we also visited Bonaventure Cemetery in Savannah, made famous by the statue *Bird Girl* that appeared on the cover of the book.

Another time, we took a fall foliage trip to New England. From Portland, Maine, at Clyde's suggestion, as he had done it before, we took a mailboat tour along the cold waters of Casco Bay, passing idyllic islands painted in many shades of red, yellow, and green. En route south we stopped in quaint historic towns: Kennebunk, Portsmouth, and Salem; skipped Boston, where we both had been many times; followed the Pilgrims Highway to Cape Cod; went out to Martha's Vineyard; then traveled westward to Newport Beach to see the "summer cottages" of the rich and famous from the American Gilded Age.

In January 2006, when Big D was cold and dreary, we flew to Honolulu, where I was scheduled to make a presentation at a conference. Twenty years earlier, on my way from Shanghai to Chicago to start graduate school at Northern Illinois University, Honolulu was my port of entry into the US. My layover there lasted an agonizing ten hours. While going through customs, US customs officials confiscated the food I had brought with me from Hong Kong: a few Dole bananas and California oranges.

"But these oranges are from California," I protested to the customs officer. Apparently, once fruit has left the US, it permanently loses its residency-right to reenter.

When I examined the McDonald's menu in the airport and calculated the dollar prices in Chinese *yuan*, I came to the shocking conclusion that a Big Mac meal would cost my entire month's salary in China. I boycotted this "capitalist exploiter," drinking from a water fountain and feeling grateful that the water was clean, free, and unlimited.

Honolulu, here I am again, with a doctoral degree, a list of professional accomplishments, a college-educated son, and a loving husband!

Between my professional duties, we paid homage to the Americans who had lost their lives during the attack on Pearl Harbor. In the solemn atmosphere of the USS *Arizona* Memorial, I silently gave my gratitude to all service members, including my husband, for their honor, valor, and services.

In the USS *Arizona* Memorial, Pearl Harbor, January 2006.

The conference in Honolulu concluded after four days, and our weeklong island-hopping cruise began. The first port of call was Kahului, on Maui, where we toured a pineapple plantation and shared a bowl of ice cream topped generously with chunks of fresh pineapple. Hilo, on the Big Island of Hawaii, was the next stop. Our bus took us all the way up to the summit of Mauna Kea, which, at 13,802 feet above sea level, is the highest point in the state of Hawaii. Near the summit, the guide pointed out a blooming silversword plant. Silversword was once abundant on the island of Hawaii, especially around the volcanoes. It had now become an endangered species and was rare to see. In Kona, we visited an old coffee plantation and passed by Kealakekua Bay, where, on February 14, 1779, British explorer Captain James Cook was killed by native Hawaiians during his third visit to the islands. We saw a peaceful stretch of sunlit beach—no sign of its violent past.

Our final port of call before returning to Honolulu was Nawiliwili, on Kaua'i. The highlight of the trip, a luau, or Hawaiian feast, dubbed the "Hawaiian cultural extravaganza," was to be held on the grounds of the Grand Hyatt. As we entered the garden where the luau would take place, Hawaiian boys and girls greeted us with broad smiles and leis. The boys wore *malos*, or loincloths, and the girls wore hula dresses, aka coconut bras and grass skirts. They all had leis around their necks, and their tanned, healthy-looking skin glowed in the sun.

Wearing our leis, we followed the other partygoers to a big lawn surrounded by flower beds. Picnic tables with white tablecloths were lined up in the center of the lawn, facing the stage for the Kalamaku show, in which hula and fire-knife dances would be performed. On one side of the lawn were long tables with big covered trays. Opposite the stage, at the back of the lawn, were tables holding glasses filled with different beverages, including deceptively sweet and fruity spiked homemade Hawaiian punch, with a name as misleading as its content. Unlike Dr Pepper's original Hawaiian Punch, which was created in California in 1934 by three guys who were not Hawaiians and contains no alcohol, this one contained enough alcohol to knock me out cold.

With the sun nearly gone, the light became hazy and indistinct, and the whole place began to feel like a beautiful yet obscure fairyland. Around us, the performers were dancing exotically to the Hawaiian music that filled the air. It seemed that everyone except me had a dangerously sweet and deceivingly innocent Hawaiian Punch cocktail in hand. The stately hotel building facing the sea, the palm trees on the sandy beach, the last glow of sunshine in the darkening sky, the trade winds and salt air, the velvety green lawn surrounded by beds of lush tropical flowers . . . together they painted an image of a world completely free of any earthly troubles. And a feast was coming!

Holding Clyde's hand, I walked over to the tables on the side to examine the food. Didn't American mothers used to tell their children, "Finish your food—think of the starving children in China"? Years ago, I had been one of those hungry Chinese children. The sight of all those trays of food was tantalizing, and I couldn't contain my curiosity. I lifted the corner of the foil covering each big tray to peer at its secret contents. There were the usual suspects: salad, mashed potatoes, coleslaw, corn, grilled chicken, and rolls, as well as local dishes such as macadamia rice, grilled pineapple, tropical fruit, lomi-lomi salmon, and as-much-as-you-can-eat poi—mashed taro root.

But where was the protagonist, the legendary kalua pig? I asked a serviceperson and was told that it was still roasting. With an image in my mind of that poor creature, nestled in layers of banana leaves, cozy and warm, slowly scorching over the shimmering ironwood fire, tiny orange flames sizzling as the grease dripped down, I steered us away from the food tables toward the drinks. On the drink tables, glasses were lined up like little soldiers in a phalanx. We selected punch for Clyde and sparkling water for me, and then sat down at a table in the very back in case Clyde needed a latrine or got bored. Soon we were engaged in casual conversation with a couple sitting at the same table. Guessing that the pig dance over the crackling fire would not be finished for a while, I decided to take Clyde to use the latrine. The man we were talking with kindly gave us directions. "Go around those drinks tables and down the stairs," he said, "then go past the tall hedges and flower beds, turn right before the wall, and you'll see it."

I couldn't see any stairs or hedges or flower beds or a wall from where we were and couldn't be sure if there was in fact a restroom nearby. I wondered if he knew what he was talking about and how many of those sweet little soldiers he had killed already. But after several tentative turns, I was able to find the restroom. It was crowded with people going in and out, perhaps trying to make room for the kalua pig that was still slowly dancing over the fire. "Baby, you go. I will be here waiting for you," I told Clyde, then added, "Don't forget to wash your hands." To make sure he had heard me, I cradled his face in both my hands, looked into his eyes, and said again, very deliberately, "I will be right here, can you remember?"

He nodded and went in hurriedly. I watched him until he disappeared inside. Then I took a few steps back and stood facing the entrance to the men's room so I could monitor every man coming out.

After a few minutes, a number of men had emerged from inside the entrance. Most ignored me; a few threw me odd looks, perhaps because I was standing too close to their exclusive enclave. Some looked at me, then immediately looked down to see if they had remembered to close their front doors as if they had something to hide (maybe they did!). Some turned to look back over their shoulders to see if the person I was waiting for was behind them. A few more minutes went by—no Clyde. I started to feel antsy. I walked a little closer and craned my neck to see if I could spot the familiar figure of my husband.

Just then, a man marched out of the men's room. I took a step toward him and asked, "Excuse me, did you see a man who looked confu—?"

Before I could finish, the man charged at me, shouting, "Your husband is drunk! He's peeing all over the place! He couldn't even find the toilet!"

"Is he OK? What is he doing now?"

"You shouldn't let him get so drunk! Shame on you! You need to take him back to the hotel. You guys have no business being here!"

Just then, Clyde walked out of the men's room. He was immediately alarmed to see that someone was shouting at me.

"What is going on, Hon?" Clyde came over to me, then turned to the man. "Don't talk to my wife like that."

The man got angrier. He turned toward Clyde, barking, "You f—ing drunkard! You don't know what you are doing. You're so drunk that you don't even know where to pee. You pissed on the floor. You're a drunkard! You stupid prick! You have no business being here."

I knew that Clyde was not able to understand what was going on, and my English had a tendency to get stuck in my throat when my emotions ran high. All I could utter was, "Hush, hush. My husband isn't drunk. He is not well."

But the angry man could hear nothing except his own roaring. "Shame on you! Shame on you both! He doesn't know what he is doing, and you don't know what he is doing. You need to take him and get out."

Clyde might not have been able to understand what was going on, but he was still a man who desperately wanted to defend his woman.

"Get the hell out of here!" he said to the angry man, while moving in front of me as if to shield me from the angry man's attack.

The angry man must have perceived that move as a physical threat. He also moved a few inches closer toward Clyde, waving his fist in Clyde's face. He was much younger and stouter than my husband, full of rage, and ready to punch. My heart raced fiercely, and all the blood rushed to my head. I struggled to pull Clyde back, screaming those desperate words, "He has Alzheimer's disease!"

Some passersby stopped, and a few of them pulled the enraged man away. Several women encircled Clyde and me. I heard their gentle words, "Are you OK?" "Do you need help?" "That guy is drunk."

I collected myself, assured Clyde that all was well, and thanked the kindhearted people. I made it through the luau, the presentation of the pig, the feast, and the hula and fire-knife dances, with a much-diminished appetite and a heavy heart. Although the incident had not affected Clyde's mood that night, and the rest of our time in Hawaii went smoothly, I was left with a lingering question:

Am I guilty of causing a public annoyance? Do we have the right to be there?

I still don't know how to answer it.

In my journey as a well spouse, I often dealt with situations in which individual rights and public interest were at odds. It is not uncommon that a person with dementia spills food and drink in a restaurant, tries to grab food from the plate of a stranger sitting next to him—it happened in one of our flights to China—talks loudly in the middle of a movie, keeps others waiting during activities, or worse. Because of such behaviors, many well spouses tend to avoid public places altogether. A feeling of social isolation and deprivation sets in, and depression follows. I fought these feelings hard, because they destroyed my sense of well-being and made me question the value of life. Within reason, and with many compromises and a great deal of self-discipline, I took on the challenges and pushed the boundaries, to continue living as actively as I could rather than putting my life on hold altogether. People complimented me for being courageous, though I am sure I stepped on some toes.

I travel the world and the seven seas
Everybody's looking for something.[29]

In the final analysis, aren't we all looking for the same thing: spending time with loved ones in the best way we can?

There were plenty of positive and even lighthearted moments during our travels. Later in 2006, Clyde's son, Will, and his wife, Loren, invited us on an Alaskan cruise. The beauty of the Pacific Northwest was appealing, and having Will and Loren with us made it emotionally more enjoyable as well as more manageable. Now Clyde had his son to accompany him to the latrine.

We saw abundant natural wonders on that cruise: magnificent glaciers radiating brilliant blue, symbolic of a lifeless eternity; unexpected rainforests, lush and full of life; thousands of salmon spawning, heroically embracing death.

One evening on the ship, after the theater performance, we decided to get a drink before retiring for the night. On the way, Loren and I went to use the restroom. Will was with Clyde, waiting outside the women's room. As Loren and I were washing our hands, the door gently swung open and a pair of eyes peeked in, followed by the nose, mouth, and then finally the whole face, wearing the sweetest smile and very politely asking, "May I come in?"

Quickly and firmly, Loren responded, "No, you may not!"

The face, quietly and slowly, somewhat disappointed but very docile, retreated. That was the face of Clyde, my dear husband, cute as a baby. His intentions to come in the women's room were completely honorable. He just wanted to be with his Hon, wherever she was.

2007. Another fall, another foliage trip with Clyde, destination this time Mackinac Island in Lake Huron. By then, five years after his diagnosis, Clyde's mental and physical abilities were seriously diminished. He needed assistance to dress, bathe, eat, and use the bathroom. But he still walked well, with me holding his hand at all times so he wouldn't go astray, and he still knew me most of the time.

Have no fear, Clyde, you have me. And off we went.

Mackinac Island had fascinated me ever since I watched a National Geographic documentary about it. A sanctuary accessible only by ferry or airplane, Mackinac is surrounded by ice in winter, but when spring comes, the lilacs burst into bloom, covering the entire island in spectacular purples: violet, lavender, mauve, periwinkle, permeating the air with their intoxicating fragrance. People first came to the island as early as the tenth century, and it has played a vital role in travel through the Great Lakes region for centuries. It has been a favorite tourist destination since the Civil War, and most of the island is now a state park. At the end of the nineteenth century, the island restricted motor vehicles to avoid the possibility that they would startle and harm the island's residents, which included horses and horse carriage drivers.

Going back in time, how marvelous!

We arrived on the island in late October, just one week before everything closed down until the following spring. The hustle and bustle of the summer season was long over, and the island was almost empty, with only a few brave souls like us wandering around.

I would have loved to get on the back of one of those regal horses, but my own horse, Clyde the Clydesdale, required my attention every minute, so I had to put that thought out of my mind. Seeing the island on bicycles was also appealing but out of the question, not safe for Clyde. We wandered the island on foot, soaking in its history and culture: from the Indians to the French, the British, the Jesuits, and the tourists; from the lilacs souvenirs, to the horses, to the fudge, and to the smoked fish that I couldn't get enough of. We explored the gift shops, which seemed to be dominated by items related to either lilacs or horses. I bought a handmade ceramic plaque that said A SPOILED ROTTEN HORSE LIVES HERE.

"Who is the rotten horse?" I teased, knowing that my Clydesdale would never kick my rear.

"Is that I?" Most Americans would say "me" in this context, but my Clyde insisted upon using "I," the grammatically correct way, and he still remembered that.

I was greatly amused both by what was written on the plaque and by Clyde's response. I called myself "horsekeeper" those days as contrasted with "housekeeper."

Clyde was cold in the late-fall weather this far north. His blood was getting thinner and his circulation weaker. We bought a weatherproof hooded jacket, in bright yellow. It was too big for him, and the color was too loud for our taste, but I couldn't complain because it was the only size left and on sale for half the original price. With it, we could do more exploring around the island.

Clyde in his "yellow jacket," Mackinac Island, 2007.

I wrapped Clyde in the yellow jacket (no sting!) and layered underneath it one by one a herringbone wool sport coat, a spruce-green cashmere cardigan, a forest-green cashmere vest, and a white cotton turtleneck. Then I tightened the drawstrings at the bottom of the jacket to stop the cold air from coming in and adjusted the Velcro on the sleeves, which were so long that they covered his gloved hands. Finally, I cinched the hood tight so that much of his face was covered, his eyes barely visible.

Soon our carriage, a horse-drawn taxi, came to take us to the Grand Hotel for tea. To climb into the carriage, we needed to step up onto a high footrest. It was quite a struggle for Clyde. Although he was physically capable, he could not grasp the verbal instructions and was having trouble balancing.

"Clyde, put your right foot up here." I put his right arm around my shoulder to support him and help him balance. Clyde lifted his left foot but did not know where to put it.

"No, no. Not this one. The other one." Now he started to shift his feet, unsure of which was the "other one."

I grabbed his right foot and tried to lift it up, but he was fighting me.

"Come on, Clyde, put your foot here." He tried to put his right foot on one of the wheel spokes.

"No, no. Not there." Using both hands, I was finally able to put his right foot on the footrest. Holding his foot in place with my right hand, I attempted to push him up with my left hand while positioning my body to prevent him from falling. After some scuffling, I got him into the carriage. Ignoring the driver's baffled expression, I got in myself and sat down next to Clyde. "The Grand Hotel, please."

As the carriage pulled up to the front of the legendary hotel, I did indeed feel as though we had gone back in time. The doorman helped us both down. When we got inside, I took off Clyde's yellow jacket. Now he was in his herringbone sport coat, a light brown with a greenish hue, which complemented my long, graceful dark brown dress with a light brown lacy bodice mash over.

Aren't we the most civilized-looking couple! I was pleased, my troubles set aside for the moment.

A harpist was playing in the vast parlor while we enjoyed our afternoon tea, a hotel tradition for over a hundred years. We sat on a green velvet baroque couch, surrounded by pastel-green paneled walls trimmed with white molding, and nibbled on sweet and savory crumpets and tea sandwiches beautifully presented on a three-tiered bone china cake stand. Chandeliers gently illuminated the entire parlor, making everything sparkle delicately: the polished wood furniture, the porcelain vases, the molded ceiling above us, and the marble floor beneath our feet. Outside the giant windows, Lake Huron rippled smoothly, in a rhythm that reminded me of a mother rocking her baby. It was a sensory indulgence taking us back to the Gilded Age, a glimpse of bygone elegance.

Tea at the Grand used to be a privilege afforded only to the rich and famous few, and now, although not inexpensive, it is within reach of many (debatably).

The scene in the 1980 movie *Somewhere in Time*, filmed in the Grand Hotel and elsewhere on the island, came to mind:

"The man of my dreams has almost faded now," says Elise McKenna. ". . I can almost see him now before me. What would I say to him if he were really here? ... There is so much to say. I cannot find the words. Except for these: 'I love you.' Such would I say to him if he were really here."[30]

How sad could one feel if the loss was just a faded dream? Clyde was not the man of my dreams in a time-travel fantasy; he was my present reality. Having had someone, shared a life together, and then losing this person, little by little, day by day, year by year, that was really sad. The nostalgic atmosphere made me wistful.

The day we left Mackinac Island, the sky was heavy and gray. The island was almost all deserted, ready to close down for the winter. Overnight, the wind had blown most of the remaining leaves off the trees, taking with it the last bits of color. The few fragments still left on the twigs quivered in the cold wind, desperately clinging to life.

But for how long? I wondered.

On the return flight, I took Clyde to the restroom. While I was waiting outside, he locked himself in and couldn't figure out how to unlock the door. The flight attendant came and rescued him. When Clyde went to the latrine again, I stood outside, holding the door ajar to prevent him from locking it. In my heart, I knew this was our swan-song trip. Our time to "travel the world and the seven seas" together had ended. I would be on my own to tread the roads I had left, over the hills steep and sheer, in the valleys deep and dark, and through the waters turbulent and treacherous.

Clyde in Zhouzhuang, a small town near Shanghai, 2004.

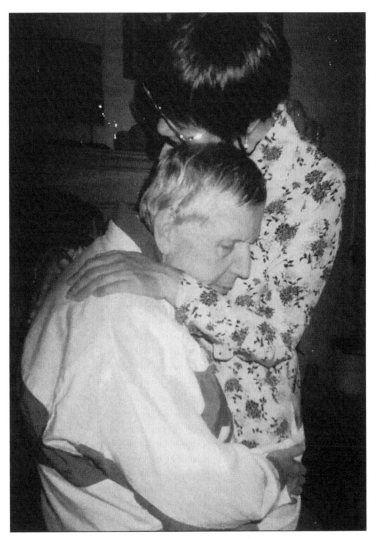

At home in 2008.

Nine

AWAY FROM HER

I never wanted to be away from her.

—GRANT ANDERSON, in the movie Away from Her

SOMETIME IN THE MID-1990S, YEARS BEFORE Clyde's diagnosis, we visited the University of Virginia in connection with my work. As a side trip to further my American education, we toured Monticello outside of Charlottesville, Virginia. The house had once been the home of Thomas Jefferson, a philosopher, scientist, historian, principal author of the Declaration of Independence, and America's third president. We walked through the house and wandered the vegetable and flower gardens where "Tom" had once labored and shed sweat. We paid homage to Jefferson at his family cemetery and took pictures with the most beautiful current residents of the estate—the peacocks, who, with their heads high and bosoms out, ignoring admirers and spectators alike, strutted freely about the grounds. Up close and personal, we were touching and breathing in a piece of American history and embracing an American legend whose ideology helped establish the foundations of the democratic government and individual freedom we know today.[31]

That day, neither of us could have imagined that Clyde would one day become a resident at Monticello—Monticello West, that is, in Dallas, the Lone Star State, far from Virginia, the Old Dominion.

Monticello West, or Monticello, as people often omitted "West," is an assisted-living facility located at the edge of the opulent Dallas neighborhoods of Turtle Creek and Park Cities. Moving Clyde to Monticello was one of the most difficult decisions I had ever made. It had been almost five years since Clyde's diagnosis, and we had entered a new stage of caregiving. By the time we returned from Mackinac Island in the fall of 2007, I knew our days of traveling together had ended. We needed to focus our full attention on Clyde's home life. Clyde's pacing, spitting, urinating, spells of agitation, and walking out of the house were becoming more frequent and harder to manage, while new and more dangerous behaviors continued to emerge. Clyde's strong desire to "do something" now included picking up objects and dropping them on the floor. The casualties were numerous: the tall Chinese porcelain umbrella stand, whose original function had been all civil and genteel—to store Chinese painting and calligraphy scrolls—but which had now become Clyde's favorite receptacle for his urinating and spitting needs; the intricately etched Waterford crystal vase on the bookshelf, a present from an old friend years ago; a pea-green flowerpot on the windowsill, holding a pink Christmas cactus; bowls and dishes on the table; lamps on the desk; framed family pictures on the dresser. Commanded by his elusive mind, as if the whole world were a hostile place filled with nemeses, his powerful hands tried to seize anything that crossed his path. Nothing was safe, and nothing impossible. Like a modern-day Don Quixote face-to-face with the windmills-turned-giants, Clyde confronted an evil-filled world populated by threatening furniture, fixtures, loose and decorative items. He pushed around tables and desks, couches and chairs, beds and dressers, anything and everything his mind failed to recognize or understand. The more resistance an object put up, the more determined he became to vanquish it. When the kitchen island didn't yield to his pushing, he subjected it to his wrath. He grabbed a mug on top of the island and started pounding the granite surface. The mug broke and cut his hand—our warrior was wounded and bleeding.

One morning, while Charlie was taking the garbage out, Clyde the Clydesdale escaped during the short interval when the garage door was open. After Charlie searched the house and realized that the horse was gone, he and Ronnie spent several agonizing hours combing the neighborhood streets in all directions. During those hours, fear, anxiety, guilt, and horrifying images filled their minds. Eventually, one of them found Clyde many blocks away. I only learned about the incident after I got home that evening and was therefore spared those terrifying moments.

I knew that no one, not even the most responsible, experienced, and compassionate caregiver, could guarantee the absolute safety of a person in their care, much less so when caring for someone with a disordered mind. I still would have chosen to continue to take care of Clyde at home, despite the challenges, had there not been another fatal blow that changed the challenges from very hard to virtually impossible.

Charlie became ill and was hospitalized.

Shortly after Charlie came to work for us, I learned that he was a cancer survivor, with his cancer in remission. He explained to me that it was a kind of bone cancer. Although I didn't fully understand it, I didn't ask for elaboration. HIPAA was on my mind, and I respected his privacy. During the two years that he had been with us, he had quit smoking and appeared to be healthy. His illness was sudden and unexpected. When I went to see him in the hospital, he was lying on the hospital bed, thin and feeble, his high cheekbones protruding between his sunken eyes and cheeks, tubes threading in and out of his body like tentacles of an octopus. It was heartbreaking to see my Charlie, good old kindhearted Charlie, who had cared for all of us, now helpless and dependent on the care of others; but it was comforting to see the ever-devoted Ronnie by his side.

"Chuck had chest pain and a fever," Ronnie told me. "He had trouble breathing."

"Does it have anything to do with his cancer?" I asked.

"The doctors aren't exactly sure. Some kind of infection. They put him on antibiotics. They don't know how long he'll be here—for a while, that we do know."

I hugged Charlie, told him that I loved him and would come to see him again, and assured him that Clyde would be taken care of. I left Charlie and Ronnie in the hospital with a heavy heart, for Charlie, for Clyde, and perhaps most of all for myself. In my sad, sad heart, I knew the time had come to move Clyde to Monticello.

Caregivers could get sick, caregivers could quit, Clyde could progress to a point where he was no longer manageable at home, or something could happen to me. For anyone, especially for a well spouse, the unexpected is most definitely to be expected. One must be prepared. Long before Charlie's illness, I had thought about what to do if I were to lose him. Would I search for another caregiver? What would happen if I could not find a fitting replacement? The bond I had with Charlie and Ronnie was so strong that for me, Charlie was irreplaceable. Even if we were lucky enough to find a good caregiver, would I want to deal with the anxiety over whether, for some unforeseeable reason, we might lose that person, too?

Or should I quit my job and care for Clyde myself around the clock?

No, I didn't want to repeat the agonizing experience of having caregivers coming in and out of my home like the figures on a Chinese revolving lantern. No, I would not willingly put myself in a situation where I had to worry about how long a caregiver would stay on the job, even if I were lucky enough to find the right person. No, I didn't want the possibility of falling in love with another good caregiver and suffering more heartbreak if he or she were to become ill. On the other hand, it definitely made no sense for me to give up my administrative position and

Chinese lanterns. By HAPPY-LUCKY.
Royalty-free stock vector ID: 1550216081,
Shutterstock.com.

tenured professorship, my hard-earned "iron rice bowl," at Southern Methodist University. My career meant a lot to me, gave me a sense of accomplishment and purpose in life, made me feel part of a larger world, and provided more than half our income. Losing that income would mean losing many choices we had, including the choices for Clyde's care. Work had been especially important to me as a well spouse because it had been a big piece of normalcy in my life.

Beyond the question of who would look after Clyde, I needed to reevaluate his living environment. If he continued to live at home, we would need to alter our habits and routines significantly, and I would face the daunting task of thoroughly upgrading our home to make it safe for him. By now, Clyde had little awareness of place. He no longer knew where he was, whether he was home or somewhere else, so I didn't expect that moving would make much difference to him. This thought freed me from the painful concern that I would be depriving him of the comforts of home if I were to move him to a care facility.

Earlier that year, when Joy and her two children came to see us, I had asked her to accompany me to see a few care facilities so that we would have a plan B should something happen to Charlie or me. We visited four or five such places, and Monticello emerged at the top of my list. Joy agreed wholeheartedly.

"You don't think this place is insufficient for your dad?" I liked bouncing thoughts off Joy, whom Clyde had described as being a person of "wonderful common sense."

"Gosh, no!" As always, Joy was positive and supportive. "It is a lovely place. Dad would be fine there."

"Since it is so close, I could see him often." I recounted the advantages of Monticello to justify my decision. "It is not too big, seems to be nicely managed, includes end-of-life care if needed, and would be affordable for us."

"Let me know if you need help." Joy was prepared to offer more than just emotional support, and her support was far beyond rhetorical. "I mean, do you need money?"

I thought about how to respond.

"Really, Hon, if you do, just tell me how much. One thousand? Two?" With a smile on her face, she added, "While I am able now."

Clyde's daughter reminded me of her dad. They were the only two people in this world who called me "Hon," reminding me of the abbreviation for "Honorable Judge" but sounding much more intimate rather than intimidating.

"Hon," Clyde had told me many times during our courtship, "if you need money, please tell me. I don't want you ever to have to worry about money." At the time, I was a single mother raising my son in a foreign land, making ends meet with a meager salary while trying to establish myself in a competitive workplace. Fortunately, in my life in the US, I had never been in a situation so desperate that I had to ask anyone for money, and Clyde had helped me in ways far beyond contributing dough. His daughter was now filling some of that emotional gap with love, care, friendship, and understanding. In my journey as a well spouse, there were times when I descended to the lowest of low points emotionally, when I wasn't able to see through the darkness beyond the seemingly never-ending suffering in my life, when I struggled to bear the perpetual demands of my husband's care, and when I felt demoralized and helpless as I watched him decline mentally and physically toward a long, slow death. I always knew I could lean on Joy's strong shoulder, trust her common sense, count on her unfailing help, or even chuckle through my tears at her wicked sense of humor. With Joy, it felt safe to discuss my doubts and show my vulnerability. She was a true friend.

I thanked Joy for her generosity. I told her that her dad, a self-made man, had always been extremely rational, thrifty, and disciplined, and had saved enough money to take care of himself in a situation like this so he would not become a burden to his children or anyone else. With our combined income, and as neither of us cared for vanity shopping, we had been able to live quite comfortably. Monticello was not inexpensive, but it was well within our means.

On a sunny day in late October 2007, not long after our return from Mackinac Island, Clyde took up residence at Monticello. My daily routine now included going to Monticello during my lunch hour as often as I could, returning there after work until I tucked Clyde securely in bed around eight thirty, then going home to the big-and-beautiful-but-empty house in University Park. The commotion and conversation that had flowed from room to room were gone so suddenly; the house felt eerily devoid of life, as if death had already happened.

I remember standing in our giant walk-in closet, finding it hard to breathe. The air inside seemed heavy and stagnant. Half the closet was still full of Clyde's clothes. As my eyes went through them, I walked down memory lane: that black-and-white herringbone wool jacket I got Clyde for one of his birthdays was the first one in his collection that was neither solid navy blue nor solid black; I had purchased the red cashmere sweater in haste one New Year's Eve on the way to the airport to pick him up; the pink shirt was the source of an inside joke—whenever he wore it, I teased, "Are you a real man today?"; that forest-green Banana Republic shirt in thick, soft cotton was another birthday present from me. I had presented it to him with a note: "You are my pine tree, big and tall, straight and sturdy, shielding me from storms and catching me when I fall."

And then there was the old navy blue jacket, tailor-made for him in Hong Kong.

"Hon, read the label." He pointed to a label on the inside pocket.

"'High Class Tailor,'" I read. "Was it made by a very famous tailor?" I was much more innocent in those days.

"Do you see how funny it is?"

"What?" I was also much slower back then.

"This is very funny, Hon. No one in the West who is high class, tailor or otherwise, would call himself that and put it on a label." He was much more cynical than I.

I finally saw the humor in it, and we laughed together. After that, we called all our "Made in China" items "High Class."

But standing in the closet now, alone, the thought of the "High Class Tailor" didn't make me laugh. Instead, as I inhaled the masculine scent that rose from his clothes, so familiar, so dear, so reminiscent of his physical presence, I began to cry.

Could it be true that this house would never again see his figure pacing

*about the rooms, never sense the vibration of his footsteps on the staircase, and
no longer experience signs of his physiology around the toilets?*

*Could it be true that I would never again feel his warm breath on the back
of my neck, or hear that deep metallic baritone voice calling from somewhere in
the house, "Hon, where are you?"*

Could I ever be happy again?

What does happiness mean without him?

What does life mean without happiness?

Holding that green cotton shirt, feeling his presence and mourning his
absence at the same time, I knelt down on the floor, curled up in a fetal
position, and buried my face in the soft, soft green cloth, sobbing.

Echoing in the background through the home sound system was a song:

> There is a house built out of stone
> Wooden floors, walls and window sills
> Tables and chairs worn by all of the dust
> This is a place where I don't feel alone
> This is a place where I feel at home
>
> 'Cause, I built a home
> For you
> For me
> . . .
> By the cracks of the skin I climbed to the top
> I climbed the tree to see the world
> When the gusts came around to blow me down
> I held on as tightly as you held onto me
> I held on as tightly as you held onto me
>
> Until it disappeared
> From me
> From you[32]

The calendar had turned to the last page of 2007. Autumn was all but
gone; winter lay ahead. Spring would most definitely return again, but

my Clyde would never return. His absence from the home we had built together was terminal, perpetual, and as certain as the yesterday gone by.

Or was it?

"There is a house built out of stone."

With the author's mom and dad in Monticello for Christmas celebration, 2007.

Ten

MONTICELLO

Life is made up of marble and mud.

—NATHANIEL HAWTHORNE, The House of the Seven Gables

A S I HAD EXPECTED, THE CHANGE OF VENUE from the big-and-beautiful house in University Park to Monticello didn't bother Clyde much, if at all. The concept of home as a tangible reality was long gone, although Clyde continued to search for a "home" that didn't exist anymore.

"Hon, take me home," he would say when I saw him at Monticello, as he had every night while he was still living in our house.

"Baby, this is where you live now," I would tell him, with an aching heart.

"Oh," he would reply. Or he would say, "I mean the other home, you know what I mean."

Yes, I know what you mean, but do you know what you mean?

It wasn't the big-and-beautiful house in University Park, the one he had just moved out of; it wasn't the little ranch on Ranchita Drive in

Preston Park before that; it wasn't the oceanfront condo in Key Biscayne, which he held on to for a long time; it wasn't the presidential mansion of Northern Illinois University in DeKalb, or the one at the State University of New York at Old Westbury . . .

The newest memories disappear first. For a while, "going home" meant going back to his childhood home in Curtis, Arkansas. *Now where?* He was in search of a place that was familiar, calm, and free of confusion; a place where he could be at ease, where he could feel at home. Unfortunately, in his Alzheimer's world, that place had forever vanished.

All day long at Monticello, the large sitting area on the third floor was filled with activity: in the morning, after breakfast, women received manicures or had their hair done; then there were chair stretches and old movie showings, with breaks for refreshments in between. In the afternoon local musicians and schoolchildren came for sing-along time, followed by another break for snacks or birthday cakes for the residents, and then more old movies, which pretty much dominated the evening as well. In the tiny cosmos of the third floor, therapy dogs never failed to make the stone-faced residents smile, and old movie reruns were never rejected.

The third floor was a matriarchal world occupied by three dozen or so women and only three men, including Clyde. All the men were still able to walk unassisted, though most of the women had limited mobility. They sat together in the big activity room for scheduled activities, day after day, but men were noticeably in short supply for the lovely ladies. All that feminine power sometimes seemed overwhelming, even in the world of the third floor.

Neither Clyde nor his male comrades seemed interested in the group activities. Clyde had never been good at following a crowd in his pre-Alzheimer's life, and he certainly wasn't going to start doing so now that he had lost the ability to understand instructions, even ones he might have been willing to follow. So Clyde the Clydesdale, my beloved horse, went on pacing from one end of the hall to the other, stopping from time to time to ask whoever—caregivers, residents, or visitors—for his sweetheart, his horsekeeper, like a foal that had not yet been weaned.

"Where is Lan Jiang?"

"Can you, can you, call . . . my wife?"

Consistently and patiently, the caregivers repeated that his wife was at work and would be there soon. Except when the horse got into trouble—then I, the horsekeeper, would get a distress call from Monticello.

So our foal continued his pacing. Clyde, in his midseventies, was the young kid on the block compared to his companions on the third floor, who were all in their eighties or even nineties. He had always maintained a healthy lifestyle and was in good physical condition, agile and slim. Frequently, as he paced, he would catch the eyes of the ladies. Every time I saw the silver-haired heads turning in unison, their eyes following Clyde as he was passing by, one of them smiling at Clyde, gesturing for him to sit by her, I smiled to myself.

Clyde didn't notice them. The song "The Girl from Ipanema" came to play in my mind, with my own adaptations:

> The *boy* from *Somewhere* goes *pacing*
> And when *he* passes, *she* smiles but
> *He* doesn't see, doesn't see . . . [33]

One evening, after having spent time sitting with Clyde and the lovely ladies in the activity room, I stood up to take him back to his own room. The woman sitting next to him held his arm and kept him sitting by her.

"He is mine." She looked at me with a sulky face.

"Can I borrow him for a while?" I said softly and smoothly, smiling, but with no intention of returning my Clyde to her.

A caregiver came to my rescue, telling the woman that Clyde had to go to the bathroom. Even the most muddled mind knew that going to the bathroom was a matter of utmost priority.

It was late morning, around eleven thirty. As usual, I rode my bicycle from my office at Southern Methodist University to Monticello to see Clyde. I biked past the restaurants and shops that lined both sides of the streets: here came La Duni, one of my favorite restaurants, offering Latin fare like yucca fries, fried plantain, and their signature tres leches cake. It was their special pastry, Guava Gloria, that had earned my undivided affection; we Shanghai women are known for having a sweet tooth. The flaky, buttery shell was finished with a shiny egg wash, baked golden brown, and covered with glittering crystals of white sugar. A bite would release the fragrant, sweet guava filling, a velvety light-yellow miracle that always sent me to heaven. I often ordered dozens of the Guava Gloria pastries to take to parties, to Chicago to share with my brother's family, and even to Shanghai, where Western pastry making began to appear at the end of the nineteenth century, when Europeans started to settle there and began the era that eventually established Shanghai as one of the most significant international cities. Pastry traditions from all over the world had been further refined in Shanghai, but La Duni's Guava Gloria was still a winner, worth showing off to my family and friends.

It was not easy to resist the temptation of La Duni and her heavenly Guava Gloria. And then there were the seductively dressed boutique windows displaying items by big-name designers or unknown ones: vanity shoes, with heels as sharp as an ice pick; perfume bottles in many colors and elaborate Moorish shapes; and fashionable jewelry, vintage and modern. Antique shops also beckoned me in to wander among exotic and mysterious items that dubiously claimed origins in the Old World or the ancient Orient.

Clyde used to call me a *looker*. The first time he said that, I thought he meant that I had "an attractive appearance," as indisputably defined in *Merriam-Webster*, but I had given myself too much credit.

"That, too," he said diplomatically, "but I also meant that you like to look at store windows without the intent of buying anything."

Well, *viva la differentia*! That personality trait made me a typical woman, and that statement made him a typical man. He found it disappointing that I could walk through five shops, look at everything, take home nothing, and call the experience therapeutic.

"I don't like to just look at things without the purpose of buying," he said while looking with his Looker in stores, again and again, patiently and faithfully.

"Would you prefer that I schlep everything home?" I said—a sensible defense.

But my midday visit to Monticello was on a time budget. I wanted to be there before lunch to help feed Clyde and those other "extra mature babies," the other residents.

Don't be a looker. Keep going! And I kept on pedaling.

Less than ten minutes later I was at Monticello West, a four-story building covered with tan plaster. From the front, it looked like a giant rectangular box, with large rectangular windows, but was actually built in the shape of a U with two short arms and a big body. It was as plain as white bread and as unassuming as cabbage and potatoes—my Chinese imagination generally goes vividly no further than food. Once through the entrance, the interior, on the other hand, was quite pleasant, even elegant. Beautifully patterned rugs lay centered on the polished marble floors. Classical moldings gracefully defined the white ceilings. Pictures in intricate frames, depicting religious scenes or landscapes, adorned the walls. Romanesque pillars stood straight and sturdy on both sides of the wide corridor that led to a spacious main dining room on the left and a great room on the right.

I swiftly passed the receptionist's desk and crossed the high-ceilinged foyer, where in the middle of the floor was a marble-topped table with a big bouquet of white Casa Blanca lilies, my favorite variety of Oriental lily. Their blooms stretched upward as if trying to touch the pendants of the chandelier, all the while releasing their insistent fragrance into the air.

No time to admire the flowers or to engage in small talk. Pushing on, ignoring the grand piano on the right in the great hall—Clyde's illness had interrupted my piano lessons—and briefly nodding to the familiar faces of men and women sitting at the tables in the dining room on the left, I jumped into the elevator before it took off with passengers already on board. The button for the third floor was already lit.

As a rule, I didn't use elevators if there were stairs. But to reach the third floor of Monticello, everyone had to use the elevator. The third floor housed residents who needed memory care. It was kept secure to prevent residents from walking out accidentally, a concept that had failed at least once when Clyde the Runaway Horse escaped.

"A Spoiled Rotten Horse Lives Here."

I reached Clyde's room. On the door hung the souvenir from our Mackinac Island trip—the ceramic plaque with the inscription A SPOILED ROTTEN HORSE LIVES HERE. I opened the door, but my horse was not in his barn.

I walked along the hallway to find Clyde and spotted him pacing at the far end of the long hallway. Something was hanging around his neck, and he was holding something under his right arm.

"What's on his neck?" I asked a caregiver who was walking toward him with me.

"Oh. He put it on and wouldn't let us take it off." She continued to walk with me. "That's a pair of his underwear."

Somehow, he had gotten hold of a pair of his undies and managed to put his head through one of the leg holes, insisting on wearing them on his top end instead of the bottom end. No one was able to persuade him to take them off. He resisted any attempt to take away his right to freedom of expression.

He had a pensive look on his face, as if he were thinking seriously about the recent subprime mortgage crisis that had reduced our retirement funds by 30 percent. His expression made him look even more ridiculous. I had to laugh.

"Baby, are you making a fashion statement? You do look nice today. Can I take a look at this?" I coaxed.

Gently, and tentatively, I tried to pull his fashionable neckwear off his head, not sure whether he would resist. He didn't. In the book *Seabiscuit*, trainer Tom Smith says, "It's easy to talk to a horse if you understand his language."[2] And that was what I, the horsekeeper, tried to do.

"Whose pillow is this?" I tried to take the unfamiliar pillow from under Clyde's arm.

"It is, it is . . . mine." He resisted, grabbing it tightly.

"He took it from Mrs. Holloway's room." The caregiver responded without having to look at it. She had already tried in vain to get him to give it back.

"Clyde, Baby, can I have your pillow?"

"No."

"He gets upset, so we just leave him alone," the caregiver explained in a matter-of-fact tone. She had dealt with all of it before.

Taking Clyde by the hand, I walked with him to the small dining room where those who required assistance with eating had their meals. Clyde could no longer use utensils. He resorted to the most primitive mode of eating, using his fingers and hands, leaving a mess everywhere. I let him pick up the less messy foods: toast, carrots, chicken nuggets, and slices of meat, and helped him with food that was more challenging for him, like mashed potatoes, pasta, turkey breast dripping with gravy, and ice cream, his favorite dessert. Clyde had a good appetite. He was often given a second serving while most others could hardly finish one.

While keeping an eye on my Clyde, who was busy picking up food with his fingers, I joined the caregivers in feeding others who were sitting there, staring at their food. Like babies, they would open their mouths instinctively if a spoon touched their lips. Among them was Sarah, a frail, shy, sweet woman who had become Clyde's pacing companion and partner in crime in getting into the rooms of other residents and messing things up. The stoic faces and skinny bodies of all these "extra-mature babies" made my heart ache with tenderness. Their frailty elicited my protective instinct, and when they gave me those baby-like smiles as I carefully put spoonfuls of food into their mouths, my heart melted.

Clyde finished his lunch. We went to his room. I turned on the portable stereo and played the CD I had made for him. It had twenty or so children's songs from a set of CDs I had bought, which featured one hundred children's songs, most unfamiliar to me. I carefully selected them from my limited repertoire of American nursery rhymes, all of which I had learned as an adult, some from raising my son Stuey in the US and most from Clyde, who had memorized a vast array of songs which he sang beautifully in his deep voice; many were classic nursery rhymes.

The oldest memories die last in the Alzheimer's patient's mind. Clyde would sing along every time he heard those old children's songs playing. As he sang, I joined him, off-key:

> *Roly Poly, Daddy's little fatty...*
> *My grandfather's clock ... It stopped short, never to go again,*
>   *when the old man died...*
> *When John Henry was a little baby, sitting on his papa's knee ...*
> *Old MacDonald had a farm, E-I-E-I-O ...*
> *Mary had a little lamb, little lamb, little lamb ...*

Clyde with Mama Wingfield, who is holding his baby sister.

The songs returned Clyde to his boyhood in the peaceful little town of Curtis, Arkansas, on the Arkansas-Texas border, where the sky was broad and the land vast. He ran free on the open meadow behind their small house, caught "gray daddies" (crawfish) down in the creek that ran by the house, and climbed high in the old mulberry tree. Dog-tired, he came home and sat on Papa Wingfield's knee. Hungrily he gobbled down the black-eyed peas with cornbread that Mama Wingfield had prepared. He returned to those days as a little boy; life was easy, no worry, no hurry. Mama Wingfield was no longer here to hold her little boy, her firstborn son and her most precious (every one of her children was her most precious, of course).

But you will always have me, Clyde Baby.

Sitting on the couch next to him, I held his left hand in mine and encircled his back with my right arm. Rocking slightly along with the rhythm, we sang in unison, in harmony.

Some words by Rabindranath Tagore flew through my mind: "Music fills the infinite between two souls."

And yes, there was a Mary who had a little lamb, which she did bring to school, in the 1800s, in Massachusetts.[35]

At some point while we were singing, Ernie, a male resident whose room was next to Clyde's, came in. I invited him to sit by my side on the couch. Ernie sat with us silently for a few minutes, then stood up and went into the bathroom. Before I knew it, I heard him relieving himself on the floor in Clyde's bathroom. I waited for him to finish before calling the caregiver to clean the floor. I discovered later that for some reason, Ernie preferred Clyde's bathroom to his own to pee, on the floor. I told the caregivers to keep Clyde's room locked to prevent that.

Sorry, Ernie.

Clyde on his pony.

In Alaska, 2006.

Eleven

THE OTHER WOMAN

*Love is a fruit in season at all times
and within reach of every hand.*

—MOTHER TERESA

I FIRST MET SARAH IN HER ROOM. It was a few weeks after Clyde became a resident on the third floor, the memory care unit of Monticello, where those with significant dementia lived. On my daily visits, since there was nowhere else to go and nothing else to do, I often walked with Clyde through the hallway of the third floor, holding his hand so he wouldn't go "astray" like a lost lamb. That day, as usual, we went from one end of Monticello's U to the other, passing all the familiar sights: the caregivers' station, the activity room, the big dining room, the small dining room, and the TV room, all interspersed with residents' rooms on both sides of the hallway. At the end of the U, we reversed direction and passed all the same rooms again. Along the way, I admired the unique décor of the residents' rooms: a current picture of the resident on the door, no longer youthful but still smiling; an antique dresser against one wall, finely crafted, probably an heirloom; a photo album lying open on a coffee table, perhaps displaying pictures of a significant event or a younger version of the resident; a cushion covered with cross-stitched red and pink roses, placed on an easy chair; a bedspread hand-quilted with small pieces of diamond-shaped red, blue, and white cloth. Monticello encouraged families to furnish rooms with familiar items to make the residents feel at home; nostalgia seemed to be the common theme.

As we passed a small room similar to Clyde's, my eyes met those of an old man who was lying on the bed of one of the resident rooms. A woman stood facing him at the side of the bed, her back toward us. I could see her silver hair and slender frame, her back slightly stooped.

"Hi, come in." The man, still lying on the bed, smiled and made an inviting gesture to us. Tall and athletically built, he had a full head of gray hair. *He seems too clear-minded to be a resident on the third floor,* I thought to myself.

The woman turned around. I saw her pale complexion and fine facial structure. She smiled at us sweetly, almost coyly, like a young girl, and said nothing.

"This is my wife, Sarah. She lives here." The man must have read my bewilderment. "I live on the second floor. Who are you?"

The second floor of Monticello housed seniors who were still mobile but had difficulty living by themselves. They were able to take care of most of their own basic needs, such as grooming, eating, and getting around by walking or wheeling themselves here and there. At Monticello, they did not have to cook, do laundry, clean house, take care of their gardens, or drive. They could enjoy as much socializing as they wished, with plenty of activities to choose from throughout the day: card games, music, lectures, dancing, exercising, crafts, and more; or as little as they wanted by keeping to themselves in their own small apartments. Unlike the third-floor residents, who seldom left the building, second-floor residents could go on outings organized by Monticello, riding in an air-conditioned van with nicely cushioned seats. They might have lunch in a local restaurant, enjoy a picnic on the lawn by White Rock Lake in the Dallas Arboretum, see a movie in NorthPark Center mall, or go shopping. The residents on the second floor had their faculties, which meant the difference between being granted freedom or being denied of it.

As it turned out, Sarah's husband was a retired lacrosse coach from Southern Methodist University, where I was working at the time. Our shared acquaintances included some of his past associates who were my present colleagues. The coach now had heart problems and was not able to do everything for himself, much less take care of Sarah, who had advanced Alzheimer's disease. They had moved to Monticello several years before: he on the second floor, and she on the third. He came to see Sarah on the third floor almost every day, although she no longer knew who he was.

"But I know who *she* is," the former lacrosse coach said.

They must have been in their mid- to late eighties. Sarah's silver hair was neatly groomed and combed back into a chignon at her nape, simple yet elegant. While most other women residents wore loose sweatshirts and baggy pants that made them, well, more or less genderless, Sarah wore more refined, somewhat old-fashioned clothing, perhaps a cream-colored cotton dress with dainty light blue flowers and a row of buttons from neck to waist. Had the coach insisted on a dress code for Sarah? It definitely was feminine. Her face had fine age lines and was very pale, a sign of lack of sun exposure. Her lips, no longer full, were painted red, as were her fingernails. It was not a bright red as often seen on flags, but a muted red that looked somewhat rusty and resembled the color of blood. It reminded me of the color Indian red, which, according to Wikipedia, was "made of a pigment composed of naturally occurring iron oxides that was widely used in India," the land of the colorful.

Caregivers groomed female residents every morning after breakfast. Their hair was done, their faces made up, and their fingernails painted. The caregiver who groomed Sarah had chosen a color that suited her well: subtle, delicate, and pleasant. Sarah always wore a vague smile. Was the expression in her eyes confusion, nervousness, timidity, or all of these?

Sarah did not mingle with the other women. Instead, she either walked alone or sat quietly, usually with one of the caregivers. I was told that she had been pestered by some of the other women residents. At the time, the cognitive world of the twenty or so third-floor residents was a rudimentary one. The fragile veneer of civilization was even more fragile because Alzheimer's hampers one's ability to inhibit behaviors, civilized or not. Did the others instinctively perceive Sarah's softness as a sign of weakness, making her, by the law of the jungle, easy prey for those tougher than she? Was Sarah the victim of her own gentle demeanor?

Were the others jealous of Sarah? After all, who else dressed so gracefully and had visits from a tall, handsome man with a full head of hair? *"Les hommes sont cause que les femmes ne s'aiment point"* (Men are the reason why women don't love each other), observed seventeenth-century French philosopher Jean de la Bruyère. And the German poet Friedrich von Schiller called jealousy the "magnifier of trifles." In the small universe of the third floor, the residents had plenty of time to spare but little ability to reason. It was all too easy for the most trivial conflicts to turn into the Battle of Waterloo.

"O! Beware, my lord, of jealousy; It is the green-eyed monster which doth mock the meat it feeds on," lamented Shakespeare's Iago.[36]

I added Sarah to our walking routine whenever I saw her solitary figure wandering aimlessly around the third floor like an apparition.

It had been a couple of weeks since I last saw the former lacrosse coach on the third floor. One evening, while walking with Clyde and Sarah, I asked a caregiver why we hadn't seen the coach here to see Sarah. "He had another heart attack. He is on the fourth floor now," she replied.

Fourth floor? One floor higher meant a step closer to life's final destination. The fourth floor of Monticello was for severely ill residents who needed constant medical care; they were bedridden and had no mobility. They seldom moved back down. More often than not, they were moved out, to meet their maker. The former lacrosse coach could no longer come to the third floor to see his sweetheart.

I looked at Sarah. She did not appear to be affected by this change. She moved around with the same frailty and quiet delicacy, wearing the same vague smile and the same hazy expression. A protective instinct flooded my heart, the kind of instinct that causes most animals to protect their young and feeble.

One day at lunchtime, I was making my regular visit to Monticello. As soon as I got out of the elevator, one of the caregivers saw me. "Where is Dr. Wingfield?" She looked around her. "He was here a moment ago. Let me find him for you."

At the far end of the hallway, I could see Clyde and Sarah walking away from us, hand in hand. The caregiver followed my eyes. Immediately, she started to rush toward them with a hasty apology. "Sorry, I didn't see them together." Before I could respond, she and another caregiver went to intercept the two. Once they did, they tried to separate them, but Sarah held Clyde's hand tightly and wouldn't let go. The caregivers must have used some force to disconnect her hand from Clyde's; I could hear Sarah's faint voice imploring, "Noooo." As one of the caregivers was taking her away, Sarah tried to turn back, her arm stretching out to reach Clyde. By now I was close enough to hear Sarah's tearful plea, "Honey, don't let them do that to me!" Her voice was shrill, as if a piece of flesh were being torn away from her.

"He is not your husband!" The caregiver grabbed Sarah's hand and shoulder firmly and continued to pull her away. "His wife is here to see him."

I took Clyde's hand, now freed from Sarah's, with her despairing, helpless voice still echoing in my head and the image of her usually serene face, twisted with fear and emotional pain, imprinted in my memory. I knew right away that the incident would leave no trace in Clyde's or Sarah's consciousness. Their dementia spared them the burden of dwelling on unpleasant experiences, a blessing of their impairment. But the incident haunted me and made me tremble for a long time.

"Some family members don't like it. We get blamed for that," the caregiver explained. "I hope you don't mind."

Mind? Should I mind? Mind what?

By nature, we human beings form attachments with each other, sometimes with strangers. Most of us are instinctively attracted to the opposite sex, even when we don't know who we are or who anyone else is, as in the case of people with dementia. It is not unusual for residents in dementia-care facilities to develop affectionate or even romantic relations with the opposite sex, even if they have spouses or partners already. In an interview with the *New York Times*, former Supreme Court Justice Sandra Day O'Connor spoke about the demands of caring for someone with Alzheimer's disease, including unexpected, sometimes bittersweet, developments. Her husband of over fifty years, John O'Connor, suffered from Alzheimer's. His deteriorating health played a significant role in her decision to retire early so that she could devote more time to his care. "He was in a cottage, and there was a woman who kind of attached herself to him. It was nice for him to have someone there who was sometimes holding his hand and to keep him company," she told the interviewer.[37]

In the 2006 film *Away from Her*, after the thirty-day no-visit adjustment period required by the nursing home, husband Grant goes to see his wife, Fiona, who has Alzheimer's disease and recently entered the nursing home. Fiona has already forgotten him. Instead, she has become attached to a fellow resident, Aubrey, a man confined to a wheelchair who has lost the ability to speak.

"It's a common tale but true," Peter, Paul, and Mary sang in "Lemon Tree." Many residents with dementia in nursing homes or assisted-living facilities form attachments with residents of the opposite sex. To make the matter more complicated, some people with dementia who form such attachments become sexually disinhibited. Holding hands and flirtation might be innocent and harmless enough, but in some instances, residents with dementia engage in sexual conduct. A mind that has lost the ability to remember or to reason does not necessarily lose the desire for pleasure, and a person with dementia may very well retain the physical ability to indulge in sexual relations. Ken Robbins, a geriatric psychiatrist and clinical professor at the University of Wisconsin–Madison, points out that "attraction, hugging, flirting, fondling, and yes, sexual relations know no expiration dates." Because we are social animals, "social connections and human touch help ward off the depression and loneliness that old age and institutional living can bring."[38]

But who gets to decide what is safe and appropriate, and based on what criteria?

It is not easy to answer the question of whether people are able to consent to sex if they can't balance a checkbook, or if they can barely speak. What we do know is that the spousal relationship is one of the most intimate, intense, and exclusive bonds between people. By chance, two strangers come together, fall in love, vow to take care of each other, and promise to be faithful. When we marry, we accept certain boundaries and responsibilities. But what happens when the ill spouse can no longer comprehend the meaning of a spousal relationship and its boundaries? After all, love is probably among the most difficult things to understand, even when our faculties are intact.

While the institution of marriage may seem to be solid in the eyes of law and other people, inside the marriage, the well spouse often descends into an abyss of emotional and physical deprivation. In *Away from Her*, Fiona's husband, Grant, and Aubrey's wife, Marian, the two well spouses, both extremely lonely, attempt a tentative relationship. They wonder, however, about the true nature of this relationship. Do they feel guilty? Conflicted? While the movie does not elaborate on that, it makes plenty clear that it was not a relationship of love between Marian and Grant, the two lonely souls.

In her article "Of Love and Alzheimer's," *Wall Street Journal* reporter Alicia Mundy tells the story of Sid. Sid was in his seventies, and his wife of more than forty years had Alzheimer's disease. He lived with his wife three days a week and stayed the other four days with another woman. While he had developed a new intimate relationship, Sid loved his wife. He had no intention of divorcing her, and was committed to taking care of her. This story generated a flurry of discussion, with people taking sides either hailing Sid as a hero husband or accusing him of adultery.[39]

Life does not always provide simple answers. Well spouses caring for a partner who is cognitively impaired and terminally ill must reconsider, most often alone, the complicated and uncertain nature of their changing spousal relationship.

So what about my Clyde and the other woman, Sarah?

The hideous disease called Alzheimer's strips away a person's facade of civilization, taking with it not only the rational mind but also the refinement and sophistication of his sense of what constitutes acceptable social behavior. What is left of the person with Alzheimer's, however elderly that person may be, is someone still seeking to connect with another human being, and still wanting to be accepted by the opposite sex. After all, connecting with another human being, especially with the opposite sex, is one of the most important desires humans have, a matter of survival and evolution of human race. My rational mind was able to see Clyde and Sarah, two beings as innocent as young children (at the time, Clyde's mental capacity was diagnosed as similar to that of a two-year-old). I rejected the idea that their togetherness was a betrayal of the marital love they had each vowed to keep. I have always considered generosity and empathy to be among the elements of true love, so I decided to accept my Clyde's "other woman." With that, the boundaries of my spousal relation were redefined and my love for Clyde transformed.

Believing that compassion had triumphed, I told the caregiver that I didn't mind Clyde's spending time with Sarah.

For the rest of Clyde's stay at Monticello, when I visited, I often found Clyde and Sarah together. Most times they were holding hands, walking back and forth. Sometimes they sat on the sofa together in Clyde's room. Clyde talked and Sarah listened. The conversation went something like this:

Clyde: "Honey, you know that, that, that . . . You know it?"

Sarah: "Yes, dear."

Clyde: "Did you, did you, see that? Did you?"

Sarah: "Yes, dear."

The two became partners in crime. They got into other residents' rooms, "stole" things, and created chaos. One time I caught them in another resident's room. Clyde was struggling to drag the bedspread off the bed. The pillows were already on the floor and clothes were scattered all over the room. Sarah was pleading softly, "Honey . . ."

There was no past or future between them, just the present moment. Neither knew the other's name, who the other person was, or where they both were, but they were often together. Clyde still recognized me and was always happy to see me, but felt no shame at being with the other woman.

I took both of them walking with me, Clyde on one side and Sarah on the other. Hand in hand, our threesome looked pretty handsome on the third floor, going up and down the hallway, passing all the activity rooms and peering into other residents' rooms. At lunchtime, I sat with them in the small dining room designed for those who had forgotten how to feed themselves. I put a heaping spoonful in Clyde's mouth, then a small spoonful in Sarah's.

One evening, most of the residents were in the TV room watching America's biggest hero, Indiana Jones, for the hundred and first time, I was sure. Clyde, Sarah, and I sat at the back by the wall, with the night-shift caregivers. "Does Sarah have any children?" I asked a caregiver. "Does she have anyone other than her husband?"

"Come, Sarah," one caregiver said to Sarah, and she walked over to her, as docile as a little girl. The caregiver reached into Sarah's pocket and took out a worn black leather wallet, opened it, and showed it to me. Inside the wallet, there were two photos: a young man on one side and a young woman on the other, both of them good-looking, both of them smiling.

"Sarah, who is this?" asked the caregiver, pointing to the man.

Sarah looked at the photo, raised her eyes, and looked at the caregiver, with her usual faint smile and expression of bewilderment and coyness, as if she were embarrassed that she couldn't answer.

The photos were of Sarah's son and daughter, her only children. Both were long deceased. Her son had died in a car crash, and breast cancer had taken away her daughter.

Unimaginable tragedy had struck this frail woman, not once, but twice.

I pulled Sarah to me and cuddled her skinny body against mine, feeling her small, protruding bones. *Sarah, the cruelty of life cannot hurt you anymore.* Sarah smiled at me, with serenity and childlike innocence, as if she were at a point of harmonious equilibrium, beyond all earthly troubles.

One afternoon when I was with Clyde and Sarah, a caregiver was rushing around, looking for Sarah. "Where is Sarah? Where is Sarah?"

"She is here. What's happened?"

"Her husband wants to see her. We need to get her ready."

They put Sarah in a forest-green corduroy dress with a white lace collar, combed her hair, and freshened up her lipstick. She sat there like a young bride being prepared for her wedding. In no time they were done, and Sarah was whisked upstairs to the fourth floor to see the coach. I wondered if the coach knew about Sarah's attachment to my Clyde, and if he minded.

Residents on the third floor could have meals in the nice big dining room on the first floor if they had visitors who could take them there. I got to Monticello early one day to take Clyde down to the first floor for lunch. Having meals downstairs broke the boredom of eating in the same place again and again, and I appreciated the greater number of food choices available there. I still liked to have a romantic date with my husband, just the two of us. No, it was not like dining at The French Room in the historic Adolphus Hotel in downtown Dallas or having a quiet drink "In some secluded rendezvous that overlooks the avenue," as in the song "Cocktails for Two," my favorite version of which was sung by Bing Crosby.[3] But it was good enough.

Upon seeing me come out of the elevator, the caregiver helped me find the two partners in crime, who most often were drifting around hallways or rummaging in someone else's room making a mess. We spotted them coming out of one room and wandering into another. By now, the caregiver knew how to divert Sarah's attention from Clyde. She gently and adeptly inserted her hand between Sarah's and Clyde's and coaxed, pointing down at Sarah's feet. "Come on, Sarah, Beth wants to see your shoes. They are so pretty." Sarah followed her finger and looked down. She had on a pair of old-fashioned flat-soled black leather Mary Janes. She smiled distractedly, and her attention drawn away from Clyde. Seamlessly, I took Clyde's left hand, which was still faintly warm and damp from Sarah's palm, and looked at him with a big smile. Happy to have reclaimed my husband!

And I froze. My heart ached as if I had been hit on the chest. A pair of lips, in that muted Indian red, embossed perfectly on the center of my Clyde's left cheek, so bloody red, so shocking!

This creature, this dear man! You made me feel so loved and adored so completely, and you belonged to me so exclusively for so long—where did you go?

Author's family in Shanghai, 1957. She is in the back next to her dad.

When we are children, our parents love us, but we must share their love with siblings, which, in my case, meant that I got a fifth of their affections. As a mother, I love my son. I gave him life. He is a part of me. But spousal love is quite different. Two strangers come together to achieve a degree of complete mutual trust, to form a bond so strong that they vow to maintain till death do they part. We are born alone, we die alone, but with this spousal love we create a sense that we are no longer alone and that we are worthy of the kind of love that belongs only to us, unconditionally.

All that now seemed to become an illusion.

In my mind I heard, endlessly chanting, an ancient Chinese lyric from *The Book of Songs*, the earliest Chinese poetry collection, known as a marriage vow in China:

> In death or in life we may be parted (死生契闊);
> With you I made this pledge (與子成說):
> I hold your hand in mine (執子之手),
> And we will grow old together (與子偕老).[41]

At the same time, I heard the echoing refrain of Poe's mysterious ebony bird:

> "Nevermore . . . Nevermore."[42]

I held back the twitch in my throat as we got into the elevator and descended to the first floor to have lunch as planned. We sat down side by side at a corner table by the window. Inside this vast, beautifully decorated dining room, well-dressed people greeted each other, chatting, eating, and

"In death or in life we may be parted ..."

laughing. To conceal my sorrow, I avoided eye contact with anyone and turned my face toward the window. Outside in the courtyard, the limbs of the crape myrtles swayed gently, red flowers and green leaves bathing in the sun, unaware of the brokenhearted observer. The beautiful scene was incomprehensible to me. My entire mind was occupied by a rhythmic, monotonous, and persistent voice:

> "I hold your hand in mine (執子之手),
> And we will grow old together (與子偕老)."

> "Nevermore."
> "Nevermore."

One teardrop rolled gently down my face, then the rest gushed out as if a dike had broken. I felt no anger, no resentment, no bitterness, no jealousy; only grief and a tremendous sense of loneliness.

Clyde sat by me, silent. The server brought our food and set it down on the table. I picked up some food with the fork to feed him. He didn't open his mouth as usual. My throat caught, and I couldn't speak. The tears that kept welling up and rolling down filled my mouth with their saltiness and blurred my vision of Clyde's familiar face.

Baby, how much I need you, how much I want to feel your strong shoulder!

Then, suddenly and unexpectedly, shaking his slightly bent head, his baritone voice full of sadness, Clyde said slowly and clearly:

"Hon, there is no one else but you."

In Alaska, 2006.

Dallas Arboretum, 2006.

Twelve

PARADISE LOST

There cannot be a crisis next week.
My schedule is already full.

—HENRY KISSINGER

2008, SIX YEARS AFTER CLYDE'S DIAGNOSIS. It was winter. Outside the window, the sun was shining brilliantly, projecting an illusion of benevolence and warmth. I intended to sleep in; on a day like this, nothing felt more luxurious than being able to stay cozy in the warm, soft bed, buried alive deep under the down comforter and leaving the harsh cold outside to its own devices.

It was barely seven o'clock when the phone rang, waking me up from the land of warmth and tenderness. I stretched deeply and reached for the phone on the nightstand, letting out a sigh.

I will be so upset if it is a marketing call!

But the word "Monticello" on the receiver's dimly lit LED screen immediately sent me into high alert.

"Mrs. Wingfield?" a familiar voice asked. "Mrs. Wingfield, I am

Deanna from Monticello." Deanna was the head of the care team on the third floor.

"Is Clyde OK? Anything wrong?" I was almost out of breath.

Every phone call from Monticello made my body tense, my head dizzy, my palms sweaty, my nerves jittery, and my heart skip some beats. There had been no good news at all, just crises and then more crises. This call was especially alarming because early morning was supposed to be a no-battle zone.

"Mr. Wingfield was very agitated this morning. He refused to get dressed, and he pushed the caregiver. We don't want to aggravate him any further. You said you wanted us to call you when things like this happen. Can you come?"

"On my way." I jumped out of bed, pulled whatever clothing was at hand over my body, leapt into the car, and off into the cold I went. My mind raced through the recent string of crises at Monticello. *What else can I do to make things manageable there? Where can I turn for help? Does Clyde's medication need adjustment? What can I do if Monticello kicks the horse out?*

Suddenly I realized that red and blue lights were flashing behind me. I pulled my car to the side of the road, feeling anxious and annoyed with myself. Although I was clueless as to the nature of my offense, I knew that being distracted had made me reckless. I had neither time nor energy for this now.

A policeman approached me. In his uniform and a cowboy hat, he looked handsome and authoritative, and he was very courteous, like those you see in the movies, a perfect gentleman.

"Good morning, ma'am. Do you know why I have stopped you?"

I shook my head, smiling at him awkwardly. When I am nervous, my English seems to get glued to my throat and doesn't want to come out. So I resorted to an automatic smile, although I really had no idea what I did or didn't do.

"Are you in a hurry? Is there an emergency?" He noticed a handicap tag hanging from the rearview mirror. It was Clyde's. "Where are you going?"

"I am going to Monticello. They just called me. My husband is in trouble." I noticed a little trembling in my voice as I handed him my driver's license. *Clyde needs me. I have no time for this!* "What did I do?"

"Ma'am, you just ran that stop sign." He pointed behind us.

"I am sorry. I didn't see it," I said, remorsefully. "I was very worried about my husband."

Maybe it was my awkward smile that moved him, but more likely, it was because of the weariness in my voice and on my face that the handsome, tenderhearted officer sent me away with just a warning ticket and some kind words, "Be careful, ma'am. I hope your husband is all right."

Salute, cowboy!

With immense relief and gratitude, I drove on, paying more attention and feeling that whatever trouble I faced, the world was still full of compassion and kindness. A few minutes later, I was on the third floor of Monticello.

A caregiver unlocked Clyde's door. I walked into a ghastly scene, a scene no one should ever have to be part of. The bed was in disarray: the pillows out of place, the blanket pulled back, and the sheets in a wrinkled pile. The sunshine outside lit up the entire room brightly. In striking dazzling white, sitting on the edge of the bed, was Clyde's predominately Caucasian body, naked, without a shred of the shroud on him, so fair, so pale, and so frosty cold. His teeth were clattering uncontrollably, and his body, not much flesh left hanging on his bones, skin slightly sagging, ribs protruding and joints bulging, was shivering from fear as well as cold. I thought of the painting *Scurvy Victims* by Nikolai Getman, a Ukrainian artist who had survived the forced labor camps in Russia. The painting depicted prisoners in the Soviet forced labor camps, the *Gulag*, during Joseph Stalin's era from the 1930s to the 1950s.[43]

"Oh, Clyde?" I cried, rushing to him. "Oh, Clyde!"

I pulled the blanket over his back and tried to wrap him in my arms and hold him close to me.

"What happened?" I was sobbing.

At my touch, his body immediately tensed up. Hugging himself with his folded arms, he raised his head, eyes frightened and uncertain.

"Are you, are you, goin', goin' . . . hurt me?"

"Clyde, Baby, look at me." I cradled his face and made him look into my eyes. Trying to stop the shaking in my voice, I repeated these words to him slowly and firmly: "I am Lan Jiang. I am your wife."

His eyes focused on mine. Gradually, his mind was able to register my face and voice. He let me wrap him in my arms and buried his head in my chest. His fine silver hair, silky and soft, brushed my chin. I pressed my lips on the top of his head, feeling his vulnerability through the softness of his hair, and clasped him tightly in my arms.

My precious man! My helpless, defenseless, clueless, lost, wounded, and terrified poor baby horse! Tears rolled down my cheeks, warm and salty, and dropped on his head. I was filled with sadness and anger.

Baby, I am so, so sorry. I promised that I would protect you. I have failed you.

I wrapped the blanket tighter around him, smoothed his hair, and caressed his back until his shivering stopped and the tension in his body started to melt.

"I am Lan Jiang. I am your wife. I am here," I repeated. "You are safe, Baby, you are OK."

I remembered reading Aristotle, who in 350 BCE wrote in his *Ethics*, "Anyone can get angry—that is easy—or give or spend money; but to do this to the right person, to the right extent, at the right time, with the right motive, and in the right way, that is not for everyone, nor is it easy."[44] I didn't know at whom I should aim my anger or where my anger should go or what purpose my anger would serve. I didn't think Monticello would mind if my anger meant that I would move Clyde out, and I didn't know who might be able to handle Clyde if Monticello couldn't. What I did know was that there was no room for me to be weak. I swallowed my useless anger, wiped off my useless tears, dressed Clyde, and prepared him for another day in Monticello. How long would he be able to stay there? I didn't know.

Deanna told me that because it was a Sunday, Clyde's regular caregiver, a beautiful, tall, kind, delightful nursing student from Kenya, was off duty. Deanna had therefore assigned a new person to handle Clyde's morning routine. Clyde looked healthy and able, so the new caregiver had assumed that he would be able to dress himself under some supervision, as some residents were able to do. She laid Clyde's clothes by him and told him to get undressed from his night garment, which, with some help, he managed to comply with. Then she told him to get dressed, but he started to mess around with the clothes and bedding, ignoring her verbal instructions and resisting her help. She didn't realize that Clyde could not understand her and thought he was being defiant. The exchange got both of them frustrated. By the time she approached Clyde to dress him, he had perceived her as a threat. The horse was agitated and about to buck. He pushed her. They locked him in his room, and Deanna called me.

Shortly after Clyde had moved to Monticello, I realized that Monticello would not be the paradise I had hoped for, relieving me of the constant worries about his care. In fact, his predicaments far exceeded my expectations, and, I was sure, those of Monticello's management as well. Understandably, his nondiscriminating spitting, urinating, cussing, and pushing were unpalatable to the administration because they were bad for Monticello's image. His spitting left visible marks all over the carpet in the common areas. His stealing and hoarding, though not deliberate, caused constant contention between him and other third-floor residents. He was not able to voice his need for the bathroom, and the two-hour bathroom intervals were not always in sync with his biological schedule or to his liking, so not only had wastes soiled his cloth, but there had been several feces crises during which feces got all over, and I really mean *all over*! It took Monticello staff hours to clean everything, not just him, but the bedding, furniture, and bathroom fixtures, and it took at least a week of daily carpet shampooing to get the smell to a bearable level. Then a few days later, it happened again, and the whole carpet needed to be replaced by Monticello.

During Clyde's bouts of ceaseless pacing, he got into other people's rooms and messed things up; he spat left and right and relieved himself behind the TV, so as to be hidden from all the TV-watching ladies, as if decency and discretion were still hiding in some remote corner of his brain; he shoved and cussed at Monticello staff members or anyone else who tried to stop him; he pushed the emergency exit door and set off the alarm, and then he fought the caregiver who wanted to get him away from the door. One day, when he had pushed the emergency exit door yet again and set off the alarm, Deanna rushed over to get him away from the exit. Clyde grabbed her by the chest, shook her violently against the wall, and threatened, "If you touch me again, I'll beat the hell out of you, SOB!"

The horse I knew had never uttered those terrible words to anyone. I apologized to Deanna profusely, who politely said that she understood it was the Alzheimer's disease, not Clyde, that was to blame.

"But we cannot continue to keep Mr. Wingfield here if we cannot get his aggressive behavior under control, for the safety of other residents, not to mention the safety of the staff," she added.

I told Deanna that they could call me anytime Clyde was having a fit—and call me they did, whenever Clyde had a fit. I could see that Clyde was a black horse on the third floor, one who commanded significantly more effort to maintain. It made me feel guilty and afraid. The possibility that the horse would kick and buck his way out of Monticello made me constantly anxious. I tried to spend more time and made more effort at Monticello, hoping to alleviate some of the staff's burden.

Yet squabbles between Clyde and other residents had not stopped. With lovely Sarah by his side, he kept getting into others' rooms, pushing furniture around, pulling bedspreads off the beds, throwing pillows on the floor, and stealing and hoarding things. Cushions, photo albums, and other trinkets that didn't belong to him showed up in his room. One time his pocket was stuffed so full that it bulged awkwardly and felt solid to the touch. After some digging, I pulled out the treasure Clyde had hidden: an XXXL-sized bra, crumpled but still plump, proudly displaying fertility and maternity!

The caregivers at Monticello knew it was better to let the horse be as long as he was not hurting himself or other people. They had learned from experience that Clyde the Clydesdale got agitated if they tried to control him, kicking and bucking like a wild stallion. But with each new incident, Clyde was edging closer to the limits at Monticello, and I was losing sleep, growing increasingly anxious. If Monticello throws the horse out, what am I supposed to do? I worked more diligently to help. I fed Clyde, I paced with him, I cleaned him and put him to bed at night. Every minute I had available outside of work, I spent with Clyde on the third floor.

After all, since Clyde had moved to Monticello, our big-and-beautiful house in University Park was an empty place to return to at the end of the day, a house without a soul.

Charlie was finally out of the hospital. He and Ronnie often came to Monticello to see Clyde. While there, they lingered and spent hours with him. They were still part of our family, and we were part of theirs. Ronnie had quit his job while Charlie was in the hospital. Now both of them were as free as birds, had plenty of time to spare, and had an empty bank account to fill. I rehired Charlie for four hours a day, Monday through Friday. It was such a relief knowing that Charlie was at Monticello preventing Clyde from getting into trouble and that Ronnie was also there, perhaps spinning his yarns and entertaining the caregivers with his nonstop animated quacking, cracking jokes and making everyone laugh. I continued to spend my evenings there, staying until Clyde was safely tucked in for the night.

A healthy body commanded by a confused mind is a dangerous thing. One morning, before Charlie arrived at Monticello, Clyde followed some visitors into the elevator. He looked so normal that no one guessed he was one of *them*, a resident, so no one questioned him. He got down to the first floor, passed the reception desk, and leisurely strolled out of Monticello onto the street, then onto the nearby busy interstate highway. The incident stirred up quite a scare for me, for his life; and for the Monticello staff, who were worried about his life as well as their liability.

Charlie and Ronnie were indignant. "You could sue Monticello for negligence," Ronnie said. "Clyde's safety is their responsibility. You should at least demand compensation from them."

I didn't. I was too exhausted to fight another war, and I didn't think it was a war I should fight or could win. In spite of my struggles with the situation at Monticello, I understood how difficult its caregivers' jobs were. To this day, I feel gratitude to the caregivers there. I didn't think that absolute safety was an attainable goal. I told myself that each incident was a battle, but that getting through each battle was a triumph.

The morning following the runaway-horse incident, the executive director of Monticello, a middle-aged man with a great deal of professional aura, summoned me to his office. "The unfortunate event with Mr. Wingfield yesterday could have had a much worse outcome," he said. "We may not be this fortunate next time."

No one could guarantee Clyde's safety, not me, not even Monticello, with its secured windows, formidable walls, and team of well-trained staff.

Mr. Executive Director went on to tell me in polite but unmistakable terms, "We don't know how long we can keep Mr. Wingfield here."

Monticello definitely had had quite enough of the horseshit.

As Clyde continued to pose challenges at Monticello, I continued to worry about when the sword of Damocles would fall. I felt like I was living in the scene of *The Rocky Horror Picture Show*, where Rocky Horror, a physically perfect muscleman complete with blond hair and a tan, artificially made by the mad scientist Dr. Frank-N-Furter, sang:

> The sword of Damocles is hanging over my head
> And I've got the feeling someone's gonna be cutting the thread....[45]

I increased Charlie's hours so that he was in Monticello with Clyde all day until I got there in the evening. When I added up what I was spending on Monticello's fees, what I was paying for Charlie's help, and the intangible cost of my time and constant worry, I started to wonder if it was worth keeping Clyde in Monticello.

But where would he go?

There were always choices but never perfect ones. Keeping Clyde at Monticello still seemed to be one of the lesser evils. *Perhaps the horse will soon be tired of kicking and bucking,* I thought wistfully.

Spring returned as expected. Summer was around the corner. I was scheduled to go to Shanghai on May 1 to give a lecture and visit my parents. Three days before my scheduled departure, the management at Monticello summoned me to yet another meeting. Since Clyde had moved there, we had had many meetings to figure out how to make the unmanageable horse manageable.

Is the sword about to fall?

My anxiety kept me awake all night. Punctually, at nine in the morning, I walked into the executive director's office. On the far side of the desk, in addition to Mr. Executive Director, were two of his lieutenants: a woman who was the manager of Monticello and Deanna, the third-floor care team head. A lonely chair was left for me to sit in across the desk from them. *A clear layout of power,* I thought. The two women, with whom I had had many dealings, seemed to greet me with more than usual friendliness.

I remembered a well-known ancient Chinese war tactic: "Show courtesy before resorting to force" (先礼后兵). I smiled back, covering my nervousness. *This is not good.*

"Mrs. Wingfield." Mr. Executive Director cut to the chase as soon as I had sat down in the lone chair for the powerless. "After much consideration, we want to let you know that we will not be able to keep Mr. Wingfield at Monticello."

"I had guessed that this was the reason why you called this meeting. I understand."

I was surprised by how calm I was. I felt almost relieved. Although it seemed like a very long time, Clyde had in fact been at Monticello for only six months. Those had been incredibly stressful months for me. I might not have known what I should do, but at least I knew that the ordeal of the past six months was over. Somewhere in the back of my mind, a voice started chanting:

> Let the wind blow and the waves crash (不管风吹浪打),
> Better than strolling in an empty courtyard (胜似闲庭信步).[46]

They were from the poem "Swimming," by the man who had once been the powerful Chinese ruler Mao Zedong. I am not a fan of Mao, but some of his poems are striking. If Mao could weather the political storms with calm and confidence, I, surely, could face my horse's being "booted out" with serenity and self-reliance.

Mr. Executive Director continued to give justifications for his decision to dismiss Clyde, with the two women listening attentively and nodding supportively.

"We've had people spit, we've had people pee, and we've had people cuss, but we have never had people who did all three. Mr. Wingfield's aggressive behavior is a great liability to Monticello. We have to watch out for other residents and our staff."

I couldn't argue with that, but was it only in my imagination that I saw a little remorse and a little apologetic expression in Deanna's eyes? *Never mind.* I asked for thirty days' grace because I was heading off to China and would be away for three weeks. They generously granted my request.

The thread was cut, and the sword had finally fallen. Now that the decision had been made, I felt free of fear and anxiety. I would find a solution for us. I had three days before taking off for China.

As a Chinese, I had grown up with this old saying, "Heaven never seals off the exit" (天无绝人之路).

It never did.

The Sword of Damocles.
"The tyrant; standing in front of his throne and holding a sword and birch; dangling above
his head the sword of Damocles; a male figure in background looking at the sword;
illustration to Petrarch, *Von der Artzney bayder Glück*, Augsburg: Steiner, 1522."
© The Trustees of the British Museum.

After Monticello, Clyde stayed in the small apartment on the right side of the
bottom floor of the house of the right. The big-and-beautiful-house is on the
left side of the left house.

Thirteen

MY! MY!! MY!!!

Life is a lot like jazz . . . it's best when you improvise.

—GEORGE GERSHWIN, American composer

IN ORDER FOR ME TO GO ON MY TRIP TO SHANGHAI with some peace of mind, I needed to settle on a new place for Clyde before I left so that we could move him immediately upon my return. I was both relieved and devastated: Relieved because the past six months had been so chaotic. Things just couldn't get any worse. Devastated that Monticello could no longer offer Clyde the sanctuary I had so desperately hoped for, and that I was facing yet another unknown.

James E. Faust, an American religious leader, once offered this guidance: "There is a divine purpose in the adversities we encounter every day. They prepare, they purge, they purify, and thus they bless." As an agnostic, I lacked the capacity for grandiose feelings such as *divine* or *purify*, but I had faced my fair share of adversities in life. I am a firm believer that hardship and misfortunes are requisites in making us stronger, smarter, and more compassionate; adversities also sometimes lead to new and even better opportunities. Disappointed and devastated though I was, I wasted no time in searching for Clyde's next placement: I was focused, determined, and full of tenacity and confidence.

Surely there will be other choices for us. There always are!

Maybe things will even get better? Perhaps there is a purpose to all of this?

Clyde was still physically active. Like an unbridled horse, he treaded restlessly, spitting and pissing at random, messing everything up, and remaining unwilling to cooperate with anyone. Bringing him home to the big-and-beautiful house would still pose dangers for all of us. Within two days, I had checked out all the nursing homes and private care homes within a reasonable distance of our house. Nursing homes, where most patients had very limited mobility, looked too depressing for my physically agile Clyde, and private care homes seemed even less adequate than Monticello to handle the destructive force of a confused mind in a strong body. By the end of those two nonstop and exhaustive days, I had not ruled anything out as impossible, yet I had found nothing promising. With one day left before my departure, I returned to Monticello disheartened and at a loss.

We were all sitting in Clyde's room. I updated Charlie and Ronnie on the latest results of my still-fruitless search, along with my concerns and dilemmas. After I finished, there was a short silence. Charlie and Ronnie exchanged glances. Then Charlie spoke, with his usual calm demeanor and sweet Texas accent.

"JoAnn, might you let me *taake* care of Clyde? All I know what to do is to *taake* care of *peeple*. That is what I *luv* to do." He became a little emotional. "You know I *luv* you and Clyde. I would *luv* to do it. Won't *y'all* let me try?"

His words, simple, sincere, and unexpected, brought me to the verge of tears. Throughout the years of Clyde's illness, I had not allowed myself to sink into bitterness, dependency, or vulnerability, for fear that the dire circumstances as a well spouse would turn me into someone I loathed to be, someone resentful, distrustful, pessimistic, and lonely. But a well spouse to a terminally and chronically ill spouse is often lonelier and more vulnerable than a spouse who is not caring for an ill partner. With Charlie and Ronnie, I felt a close kinship that was rare and precious among people not related by blood. Families, both Clyde's and mine, had been understanding, supportive, and genuinely caring. But they were hundreds or even thousands of miles away, busy with their own spouses and children, their jobs, and problems of their own. Knowing that they would help me if I needed them gave me great comfort, but I was conscious that I had no right to impose on them. For years, Charlie and Ronnie had been my first responders; they were reliable and accessible, here and now. Now, once again, I felt the power of our distinctive and reassuring kinship.

"Charlie, I had not been able to bring myself to ask you to take this on. You are still recovering. Wouldn't it be too physically demanding for you? Wouldn't it be too much of a sacrifice for you to be away from your own home? I know how close you and Ronnie are. I don't want to take you away from him and your three puppies. We don't know how long this situation is going to last."

"Chuck and I have talked about it." Ronnie spoke with rare solemnity. "We love you, and we love Clyde. The happiest moments we've had have been with you guys. You are like a sister to us. Chuck wants to do it, and I want to help."

That was right. I had, in fact, long been half-jokingly calling both Charlie and Ronnie "Bubba," a Texas Hill Country term for brother, and they had called me "Sissy," the female version of a bubba, a sister.

The following day, I signed a lease for a small one-bedroom apartment on the first floor of a small house just two doors down from our big-and-beautiful home on the same side of the same street. Just like that, Clyde's post-Monticello care plan was settled, and it was better than I could have hoped for. I left for China knowing that as soon as I returned, Clyde would have a new place close to me, and we would have Charlie and Ronnie by our side.

I left for Shanghai with a renewed appreciation of the wisdom of my ancestors:

"Heaven never seals off the exit (天无绝人之路)."

Clyde's seven tumultuous months at Monticello ended early in May 2008, only a few days after my return from Shanghai. The process of relocation kept us busy for several days: packing up Clyde's things at Monticello, furnishing the small apartment where he would be living, and moving everything to it. All this activity diverted some of our attention away from him. The second day after he and Charlie had settled into the apartment, Charlie alerted me that Clyde was constipated. It had been five days since his last bowel movement, and he was not able to relieve himself.

Charlie and Ronnie laid Clyde down on his side in the bed and tried to unclog him. But by then Clyde's bowel was corked as tight as a bottle of wine, properly sealed and over-aged. When Charlie touched the plug, which bulged visibly, the bottle whined in pain. I asked Charlie to move Clyde a little so he would be lying more on his belly, hoping that a different position might make the cork a little easier to pull. But the move made Clyde groan even more. Charlie stood there, unable to proceed and uncertain what to do. I was sure that in both of our minds was the same expression, and it was not "pain in the *neck*."

My memory flashed back more than twenty years earlier to a hospital in Shanghai. My first husband was severely injured, and one of his arms had to be amputated. I was asked to sign the form giving consent for the doctor to perform the surgery, which was necessary to save his life, but the form stated that my husband could die during the operation. At thirty-one, with a one-year-old baby, I couldn't do it. I couldn't hold the pen in my hand and sign off the arm and maybe the life of my infant son's father. It was my forever-sensible and heroic mother who stepped in and signed the consent form on my behalf.

But my mother is thousands of miles away in China. She cannot do this for me. I have to do it. I must do it. It must be done!

As Charlie cautiously turned Clyde's back a little to get him out of his awkward and uncomfortable position, Clyde howled louder than before.

"Maybe we ought to take him to the emergency room," Ronnie suggested warily.

"You may be right. But I am afraid that would prolong his pain and even make it worse." To most Chinese, constipation does not constitute a big enough problem to go to a doctor. We don't always go by the book, much less by the book in a foreign language and by a foreign culture. Many a Chinese mama of my generation would have had the experience of manually opening her baby's stopped-up bowel.

And I am a Chinese mama!

I put on a latex glove and, tentatively and delicately, pressed the cork. It was as hard as a rock, and the bottle shrieked in pain at even my featherlight touch. I paused, taking a moment to assess the situation, making quick and intuitive calculations in my head. *What will be the cork's power of resistance? How much force will be needed to break it? What will be the best angle, and how deep should I go?* Fighting the vivid images in my mind and the *ghost pain* in my own body—that empathetic sense we human beings tend to experience when we have the sensations of others in our own body, and supplied with plenty of petroleum jelly and determination strong enough to demolish a mountain, I hardened myself physically and mentally, took a deep breath, held it, and firmly and steadily dug my finger into the hardest part of the cork.[47] Clyde bawled as if he were being butchered alive, tearing my guts apart. Chunks of broken "cork" unwillingly came out, mixed with oozing crimson fluid, staining my hand and the sheets underneath. Flowing no red wine—I had my husband's blood on my hand.

Even today, when I think about that incident, the images of the incident and echoes of Clyde's wailing still haunt me. *Did I do the right thing?* Nietzsche had figured this out a long time ago when he said, "You have your way. I have my way. As for the right way, and the only way, it does not exist." Unfortunately, in the day-to-day routine of caregiving, a well spouse often lacks the luxury of knowing what constitutes the "right way" of doing things. I did the best I could, I am sure only of that.

The ordeal prompted us to follow this motto vigilantly: Two Days No Motion, Purgative in Action!

It is an old Chinese tradition to place on newlyweds' doors the symbol of "Double Happiness," a large character in bright red that is supposed to bring the couple a double portion of good fortune, joy, and harmony. For us, during those first days in the apartment, we greedily wished

A traditional double happiness sign.

for "Triple Happiness": Clyde's snoring, his pacing and messing things up, and his bowel movements. Snoring gave the caregivers a break; pacing and messing things up meant Clyde was well; and oh, boy! Clyde's bowel movements made everybody elated, while the lack of them worried us all.

The apartment was sparsely furnished with a single bed for Clyde, to make it easy to dress and undress him, and a queen bed for Charlie, so Ronnie could stay overnight if he wanted. The doorknobs were taped up to prevent the horse from accidentally escaping, and everyone went in and out with a key. The kitchen range looked oddly bare without the knobs, which Charlie had pulled out and hidden away so that Clyde couldn't "play with the fire."

One day Charlie was off duty, and I was in the kitchen fixin' Clyde lunch, as they say in Texas. I could hear Clyde moving things around in the living room, which was his usual activity to amuse himself. Then I heard him scream. Rushing to him, I found him squeezed between the door and the futon. He had somehow managed to lift the futon and make it stand up on one of its armrests. It had then tipped over, pinning him against the door. Fortunately, the futon was mostly made up of light foam blocks, so Clyde was scared but unharmed.

I rescued Clyde from the evil futon couch with a triumphant smile on my face. *Yes! The horsekeeper has outsmarted her horse.* It would have been a bad accident if it were a heavy couch that had hit Clyde.

One morning in June, a few weeks after Clyde and Charlie had settled into the apartment, Clyde wouldn't wake up. Charlie got him out of bed and sat him on the couch. He didn't open his mouth for food, nor did he get up to pace around the apartment. In fact, he didn't even open his eyes. Such sleepiness was not normal for him, so we called the doctor, who paid us a visit right away. After she had finished checking Clyde for this and that, she announced her verdict. "Clyde has had a stroke, which is evident from the paralysis on his left side." The left side of his face was slightly droopy, his left arm had stopped moving, and he was unable to keep his balance sitting down, leaning in every direction. "Three months, no more than six." She issued a sentence and put Clyde under hospice care. "I could be wrong, but in most cases, patients have lived a shorter time than I have predicted."

She went on to advise me that it was time to get Clyde's end-of-life affairs in order because when the inevitable happened, family members would have neither time nor energy to deal with legal and logistical matters on top of the emotional loss. She left me the contact information for a chaplain.

I didn't know what a chaplain could do for me. I was unclear what a chaplain did, period. But I contacted him right away to find out if he could make my life a little easier. The chaplain was a mild-mannered, clean-shaven, and kindhearted man, possibly in his forties. He inquired about my spiritual beliefs, to which I responded that I was not religious. Politely, I clarified that I was not an atheist but an *antagonist*. Seeing his apparent puzzlement, I corrected myself: I was an *agnostic*. He was relieved.

"I have a hard time sorting out those two words," I explained. "I used to be both an atheist and an antagonist. I have learned to be humble now that I am older."

To me, anyone who has lived a truly interesting life knows that life is full of unknowns. The British poet Tennyson has explained my views on religion in these verses:

> For nothing worthy proving can be proven,
> Nor yet disproven: wherefore thou be wise,
> Cleave ever to the sunnier side of doubt,
> And cling to Faith beyond the forms of Faith![48]

The open-minded chaplain accepted my godlessness graciously and religiously visited me every week until we ran out of topics to talk about. I did follow his advice to find a permanent resting place for Clyde. Yun, my sister from Shanghai, was visiting me in Dallas during that time. With her by my side, I finally mustered enough resolution to face the inevitable. I signed a contract arranging for Clyde's cremation and settled on a burial site. With both my parents still living at the time, I had never experienced death so close and personal. But having everything in place was definitely a relief.

Three months passed, then six. Clyde did not stop for Death, so Death kindly stood aside for Clyde. Physically, he had regained some strength. His left side was weaker than his right, but he was able to move all his limbs, sit safely in his big blue geriatric chair, mutter words that were occasionally intelligible, and grab everything within reach of his right arm as if it were covered with Velcro tape. On nice days, we pushed him in a wheelchair out to Williams Park. While Clyde sat in his wheelchair next to us, Yun and I sat on a park bench sipping our cups of black joe. We watched ducks swimming in the small pond, their population flourishing, but Clyde no longer spoke their language—no more quacking to make me laugh.

2008 was drawing to a close. That year, in my adopted country of the US, the global financial crisis led to an unprecedented government bailout totaling nearly one trillion dollars over the course of 2008 and 2009 to prevent the collapse of the US financial system. On May 12, in my native country of China, an earthquake occurred in Wenchuan in the province of Sichuan. At a 7.8 magnitude, it killed more than 87,000 people, injured 374,643, and left homeless between 4.8 million and 11 million. While events on such a large scale could leave people at a loss over what to think or feel, new medical and scientific advances could give people new hope: if Thomas Beatie, the world's first pregnant man, could give birth to a daughter on June 29 of that year, perhaps a cure for Alzheimer's disease was not far off. That year, the International Society to Advance Alzheimer's Research and Treatment (ISTAART) was founded with the purpose of bringing together scientists, physicians, and other dementia professionals to concentrate research on the cause and treatment of Alzheimer's disease and other dementias.[49]

My small world went on as caring for my ill spouse continued to take the center stage. It was a typical winter morning outside, cold and dreary. Ronnie told me that Charlie had not been feeling well for a few days. He had a lump in his throat and was having difficulty eating.

"Charlie, why didn't you tell me?" I was worried. Knowing his health history, I had been careful not to overload him with chores.

"I was hoping it would go away. I didn't want you to worry," Charlie said. His tone was matter-of-fact, but I could feel his helplessness.

Charlie, sweet Charlie! My heart tightened. You never complain, and you are always looking after others.

"How long has it been now? Can I look at it?" I sounded like a doctor or a sister or both.

I had, in fact, been one of those "barefoot doctors" when I worked as a peasant girl in Inner Mongolia during the Chinese Cultural Revolution.[50] For that reason, I felt that I could treat a few simple ailments better, or maybe just more audaciously, than most people, and I seldom hesitated to try my skills. While I was living in an impoverished remote farming village in Inner Mongolia, my older brother, who was in the same village, came down with a severe case of acute tracheitis and bronchitis. He was feverish and coughing up blood. There were no doctors or medical facilities anywhere near the village. I consulted my book and decided to treat him with acupuncture. The treatment required that I poke a long needle three inches through the skin between his collarbones and down along his windpipe. Any mistake and I would have punctured his trachea, causing unimaginable damage. It was the first, and only, such highly skilled procedure I ever performed. Afterward, my brother got visibly better, and no one ever disputed that his recovery was due to the superb healing skill

The author and her brother as peasants in Inner Mongolia during the Cultural Revolution.

of the barefoot doctor rather than to the robust immune system of his young body.

Charlie was like a brother to me—he was my bubba, and I his sissy; and now I even wore shoes: quite an upgrade in my status as a healer.

"It has been three or four days. It's growing big, and I can't swallow." Charlie responded to my questions as if he were talking to a real doctor.

I pulled him by his arm to the window. He opened his mouth, and I turned his head toward the light. In the back of his throat was a lump the size of a Ping-Pong ball, blocking more than two-thirds of his throat.

"How come you didn't tell me? How could you let this thing get so big! Of course you can't swallow. You must go to the doctor right away." One look at that ugly mass, and my confidence in my ability to play doctor immediately went out the window. I was terrified. Seeing the size of that monster tumor, who wouldn't have been?

"Don't worry about Clyde. I will be here." With that, I pushed both of them out the door.

Weeks later, after many tests, Charlie's verdict came back: cancer. With my limited medical vocabulary in English, I found Ronnie's explanation of the kind of cancer Charlie had quite convoluted and hard to understand, but I understood it was somehow related to his immune system. Charlie would be fighting for his life. He needed to undergo treatments that would be torturous and continuous, including chemotherapy and radiation. Ronnie would need to take care of him. Their availability for Clyde and me would no longer be dependable. Yet I knew that, more than at any other time in their lives, they needed an income, they needed support, and they needed to sustain their confidence in humanity, to know that the world was a compassionate and caring place.

What should I do?

What can I do?

Can I do it?

Things appeared, overall, to go on as normal. During the day, Charlie and Ronnie went back and forth between the apartment and the hospital. They took care of Clyde between Charlie's treatments and stayed with him at night. I filled in as much as possible and hired temporary helpers. But things were not normal. The apartment was absent of laughter, conversation, our constant teasing of Clyde or each other, and the hardly serious bickering between Charlie and Ronnie. The liveliness we had always had among us was gone. I could sense that Charlie's illness and the future of his employment were weighing heavily on them. Everybody got quieter except for Clyde, who kept up his usual muttering. We avoided each other's eyes and kept out of each other's way. They understood that I needed time and space to think; they waited, holding their breath.

After a few restless nights, I was ready to announce my decision. Charlie and Ronnie sat on the futon in the apartment living room, and I sat next to Clyde, who as usual was in his big blue chair. On the television, *Little House on the Prairie* was running. I was watching it for the first time, though Charlie and Ronnie had probably watched it a hundred times. Laura Ingalls was saying: "I knew there would be rivers to cross and hills to climb, and I was glad, for this is a fair land, and I rejoiced that I would see it."[51]

"We all know that's life, don't we?" I started. "Let's have a conversation now." And I turned off the TV.

"I know you have been wondering how we would move forward. It has not been easy for me to decide, but when I looked deep into my heart, I knew I couldn't let you guys go. Not at a time like this. You have been with me for the past several years. Together, we have been through some of the most difficult times in my life, and I feel very fortunate that you have both been here to help. I know you need me now, and I want to be with you just as you have been with me when I was most in need. So if you would like to stay with Clyde and me, we will come up with a plan."

"JoAnn, I ain't have no problem. I can continue to taake care of Clyde," Charlie said feebly. I understood that he needed to believe that, though I wasn't sure if he actually did.

"Between Chuck and me, we will get it done," Ronnie added. But I knew that was more of an intention than a resolution.

For me, moving forward together was not only an intention; it was a resolution and a commitment. I was not naive. I had experienced losing Charlie's help when he was ill the last time. And I knew that cancer, whatever kind it might be, was a very serious matter. Retaining Charlie and Ronnie would mean losing reliable help for Clyde and would require more energy and extra money from me. I had to be prepared for additional stress in the face of the inevitably competing demands of Charlie's care and Clyde's. I wrestled for days with the thought of getting another caregiver to replace Charlie or finding a nursing home for Clyde. But in the end, I knew that leaving Charlie and Ronnie financially devastated and emotionally stranded while Charlie was fighting cancer—neither of their families accepted their homosexuality well; neither was likely to offer much help—would weigh heavily on my conscience, more than my fragile conscience could bear without feeling hugely disturbed. In that regard, my decision was hardly altruistic.

"It will not be easy for any of us," I said. "Ronnie, you and I will need to work extra hard. We are the well spouses."

It was hard to tell how clearly my words registered with Ronnie. But later on, when Charlie's treatment took both of them away almost all the time, leaving me alone to manage scheduling caregivers, to struggle with paying for multiple caregivers, to juggle the last-minute caregiver cancelations, and to deal with unforeseen and unpleasant situations without the consistent and accessible support from the "bubbas," the perspective that this arrangement had been my choice kept me from becoming bitter and resentful.

And Laura Ingalls's words that morning kept me grounded: "I knew there would be rivers to cross and hills to climb. . . ."

Predictably, Clyde continued to give us a hard time. But his sensibilities sometimes caught us by surprise. He needed to be taken to the bathroom every two hours; there, the caregiver needed to pull down his *britches*, as Charlie called his pants, and to sit him down on the toilet. Getting him to sit on that ugly, odd-looking object was like a tug-of-war: we won by tipping him off balance so he would "fall" on the toilet; and he won by resisting our efforts, standing while relieving himself and soiling his *britches*.

One afternoon I went to the apartment to take over for Jamal, the daytime substitute for Charlie and Ronnie. He told me that Mr. Wingfield had refused to let him pull his "britches" down.

"Mr. Wingfield said that it wouldn't be appropriate."

"What did he say?" I wasn't sure I had heard right. Clyde had not said anything for a while that made any sense.

"He said, 'It wouldn't be appropriate.' He held on to his pants and wouldn't let me pull them down. I tried several times."

That was my old Clyde speaking, courteous, sophisticated, and gentlemanly to the last breath, with a very wet *tush*.

It was my day to put Clyde to bed. I stripped Clyde's day clothes off, leaving only his worn white cotton T-shirt and his boxers. Sitting him on the edge of the bed, wrapping my right arm around his back and positioning my left arm under his legs, I mustered all my strength and, with one sudden move, hoisted, or perhaps more accurately, yanked his body onto the bed. Almost simultaneously, I swung him a full ninety degrees to line his body lengthwise with the bed to lay him down.

"I am going to kill you!" Clyde yelled angrily, loudly, and clearly, swinging the fist of his still-agile right arm at me.

For a fraction of a moment, I was taken aback by his sudden anger. But I quickly realized that he had just been scared by the unexpected sudden move. I, on the other hand, felt triumphant at having just completed a task that was so tremendously physically demanding and pushed me to my limit.

"Oh, yeah? Then who is going to take care of you?" I bantered with my wannabe killer. "Wouldn't be prudent, Clyde."

I tucked him in and lay down by his side. While brushing his hair out of his face, I felt his warm breath on my arm and hand. Quietly, I scrutinized his expression. His thin gray eyebrows furrowed slightly. He looked like a pouting child.

"Are you mad at me, Baby?" I tried to smooth the folds on his forehead. "You can't even remember what was making you mad, can you?"

My violent act that had made him angry to the degree he wanted to kill me had already been gobbled up by the Gobbledok as if it were a Smith's Potato Crisp.

"Chippie, chippie, chippie!"[52]

Spring 2009. It had been almost a year since Clyde had started hospice care. On a sunny morning precisely at nine, Nurse Betty promptly reported for duty. She was an ample, cheerful woman, fair skinned and brunette, probably in her late thirties, who talked loudly and laughed freely, blending in effortlessly with the assorted personalities of my collective family and friends. She came to the apartment several times a week. While she was there, she chitchatted with Charlie and Ronnie, trading jokes, gossip, and Texas tall tales. Usually, Charlie and Ronnie would already have done the hard work, such as bathing, lifting, and toileting. Nurse Betty knew that her visits would not be as strenuous as those with many of her other patients, and there would always be laughs.

On that day, Nurse Betty wore heavy makeup, bold, bright, and brave, with big glittering earrings and a matching necklace. She had on a tight-fitting pink top and a pair of even tighter floral leggings with big splashes of pastel pink, blue, green, and yellow. Over her form-fitting outfit she wore a long, loose floral blouse in a sheer and barely visible fabric. Her plumpness was prominently displayed.

Upon the entrance of this floral vision, Ronnie threw a glimpse at Charlie, who returned it with a stifled smile. I knew exactly what the devilish two were saying to each other: *Look at her!* They, especially Ronnie, were merciless judges of other people's fashion sense.

Nurse Betty was even more cheerful that day. She was giddy. Spring sometimes has that effect on people's mood. It is the season to feel youthful and happy; the season to fall in love. Clyde was the first patient on her schedule. She was fresh and not yet tired. She greeted Clyde with a big grin. "Good morning, Mr. Wingfield. You look nice today."

"You know, you know . . . him, both ways?" Clyde, sitting in his big blue chair, gabbled with whatever words popped onto his tongue, pointing his right hand in the air.

"We know him all too well, every way," I chimed in. Charlie and Ronnie laughed.

"That's right, Clyde. We all know him very well," Ronnie added. "How can we not?" Ronnie winked at me. He knew exactly whom I meant: Clyde the Troublemaker!

Charlie and Ronnie were sitting on the futon, and I was sitting on the chair to Clyde's right, about to leave for work. I stood up to let Nurse Betty sit by Clyde so she could perform her routine.

In front of the chair, Nurse Betty unloaded her collection of bags, one with medical gadgets, one with binders, notebooks, and forms for recording each patient's condition, and one with her personal essentials. Then she plunked herself down on the chair.

After catching her breath and exchanging a few pleasantries with us, she prepared to check Clyde's vitals. She stood up in front of his big blue chair and bent down to reach inside one of her bags to fetch the gadgets: thermometer, stethoscope, and so on. In doing so, her *derrière* was squarely in front of Clyde's face. As she was laboriously rummaging through her bag, Clyde reached out his right hand slowly, steadily, and almost stealthily. He set it firmly on that mound of flesh. Pressing down and grabbing slightly, with plenty of pleasure, I was sure, he uttered, "My! My!! My!!!"

Laughter exploded in the apartment. Ronnie rolled back and forth on the couch. I doubled over, out of breath, and Nurse Betty fell back onto her chair, wiping away tears. Charlie was the only one who was able to keep his composure, making sure that the tubes delivering chemo into his body would not fall out of his arm.

In his big blue chair, Clyde sat, looking straightforward, seeing nothing and hearing nothing, as if he was wondering, *What's funny?*

Charlie during the chemo, 2008.

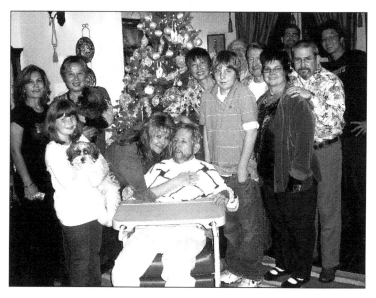

Thanksgiving 2008. From left to right, Nada, Gabriel, Yun, Joy, Clyde, the author, Collin, Joy's husband, Joe, Loren; Joe's son, Will, and Stuart, 2008.

Fourteen

FAMILY, FRIENDS, AND STRANGERS

Sometimes you have to give yourself permission
to not be hardcore for once.
You don't have to be tough every minute of every day.

—MEREDITH GREY, Grey's Anatomy

MANY EMOTIONAL CHANGES HAPPEN WHEN one becomes a well spouse taking care of a partner who is chronically and terminally ill. Relationships with others, including family, friends, and even strangers, all need to evolve; and the well spouse must come to a new understanding of himself or herself as well. Well spouses require greater support and acceptance from the people around them and need to recognize that they should not do everything in isolation. In the hit television series *Grey's Anatomy*, Meredith Grey, played by Ellen Pompeo, said, "It's okay to let down your guard. In fact, there are moments when it's the best thing you can possibly do—as long as you choose your moments wisely." Most often, those "wise" moments are the moments when one is with family and friends. Learning when to ask for help, or simply for acceptance, is the first step toward coping with crises as well as everyday challenges. Superman and Superwoman are only possible in movies. In reality, even those who are truly hardcore among us need breaks from being tough in order to build up reserves of inner strength to call on during the hardest times.

The path toward Clyde's diagnosis started with his vision. For years, he had complained about not being able to see well even with his glasses. For such an avid reader, this was a major predicament. Eventually, he had cataract surgery at the distinguished Bascom Palmer Eye Institute at the University of Miami. The surgery went flawlessly, but Clyde still had trouble reading and seeing clearly. That led him to a neuro-ophthalmologist, then a neurologist, and finally a psychiatrist. A battery of tests and much scrutiny by doctors with various specialties eventually led to the gloomy conclusion: Alzheimer's disease. The verdict saddened but didn't shock me. There had been other signs, some of them perhaps apparent only to a spouse. Nonetheless, we immediately scheduled another assessment by a widely renowned neurologist specializing in memory disorders and Alzheimer's disease at UT Southwestern Medical Center in Dallas. He confirmed the diagnosis of Alzheimer's.

That day, driving home from the doctor's office at UT Southwestern Medical Center, Clyde said to me, "Hon, promise me. I don't want anyone to know about my diagnosis." He was more concerned about his privacy than his condition. Illnesses that negatively affect people's cognition, such as Alzheimer's, often carry such stigma that it may lead others to form unflattering or inaccurate perceptions about the person who is ill.

"Of course. It is nobody else's business." I agreed wholeheartedly.

"I mean not even my children. I don't want anyone other than you to know about this."

I was surprised. I believed that family was not just for Sunday brunches and holiday feasts but also for times when one was sick, in trouble, or otherwise in need. I also believed that parents had an obligation to disclose hereditary disorders to their adult children, and that adult children had the right to know. Cautiously, I asked him, "But Baby, don't you think you have a responsibility to let Will and Joy know?"

"I am not convinced that I have Alzheimer's disease. I feel just fine," he said willfully.

I went silent. I didn't know what to say.

It is not uncommon for Alzheimer's patients to go through a denial period. Was Clyde in denial, refusing to accept this cruel reality? Was he fearful of social stigma? Or was he incapable of comprehending the seriousness of the disease? I couldn't tell. The conviction that his children had the right to know weighed heavily on my mind. Although it was clear that Clyde's judgment was severely impaired, there is no distinct threshold for mental incompetence in Alzheimer's patients. Usually, medical professionals declare a patient mentally incapacitated after the person has lost the majority of his or her cognition. Before that time comes, for a period that may last years, an Alzheimer's patient can linger between coherence and incoherence, appearing to be lucid when in fact he or she is not. To cope with this uncertainty, a well spouse has to wade through the muddy waters of legal and moral ambiguity.

At what point should I consider myself Clyde's alter ego? Ultimately, it would become evident that the former university president had lost all his faculties—no pun intended. But before that time came, what was the right thing for me to do about informing his children?

Maybe he just needs some time to be ready.

By the time we reached home, with no more hope that Alzheimer's was an incorrect diagnosis and with many new unknowns ahead of us, I had made the following resolutions:

1. Not to bring up the subject of Alzheimer's unless it was necessary. The disease did not have to rule our lives, not yet.
2. To live as normal and full a life as possible for our remaining time together.
3. To fight every battle with Alzheimer's disease that was worth fighting.

Spring 2003. More than six months had passed since Clyde's diagnosis. In our Ranchita home in North Dallas, after breakfast, Clyde was again pacing through the house, peering into all the rooms and trying to figure out things, places, and people that had become increasingly unrecognizable to him. He reminded me of Shakespeare's *King Lear*:

> . . . I fear I am not in my perfect mind.
> Methinks I should know you, and know this man.
>
> Yet I am doubtful: for I am mainly ignorant
> What place this is; and all the skill I have
> Remembers not these garments; nor I know not
> Where I did lodge last night.[53]

I was sitting at the breakfast table with Will and his wife, Loren, who were visiting us.

"What is Dad doing?" Will asked, wondering why his father, the articulate orator, was not sitting with us at the table talking politics or history or economics or philosophy, as he always did.

"I think he is looking for something," suggested Loren, plausibly.

I didn't say anything right away, but my mind was spinning. *They don't know. Should I tell them? Would it be a betrayal? Would I be breaking my promise to Clyde?* I wasn't sure whether my silence to his request of not telling the children constituted a promise or not.

But children need to know. They have a right to know.

But how should I break this painful news to them? How will they react?

I knew I had to be the messenger now, for my Clyde was hardly aware of his Alzheimer's disease. He was no longer capable of comprehending what might happen to him or his family. Clyde had entrusted me with power of attorney and had named me as his guardian. To protect his well-being, I needed to begin acting on his behalf and bearing the burden of his responsibility to people related to him.

"Do you sense something wrong with your dad?" I asked, doing my best to be tactful.

Will and Loren looked at each other, then both heads turned to look at me, wondering where I was going with this question. During the early stages, it may not be easy for people who visit only once in a while to recognize that someone has Alzheimer's disease. We all get forgetful and confused, and some of us, like me, are often absentminded. Alzheimer's is something people make lighthearted jokes about, to tease each other or in self-deprecation, until it becomes a reality.

"Jo, are you trying to say something to us?" Will was the only person who called me Jo. Until he did, I didn't know that Jo was another alias of JoAnn. And Will was alarmed by my question. "If there is anything wrong with Dad, you should tell us."

"I am not supposed to tell you. Clyde made it clear that he didn't want me to tell anyone. He specifically asked me not to tell his children." I didn't intend to keep Will and Loren in suspense but felt some degree of ambivalence about whether I was breaking my promise to Clyde, even though my rational mind had given me permission to do so. I needed to set the stage. Clyde's children and I had always trusted each other. I wanted to make sure that what I was about to say and how I said it would not jeopardize that trust.

"Clyde said that he would tell you at the right time, but I am afraid that the right time for him has passed. He will never remember to do it now." I paused for a moment. "I love him, and I care about his children. I feel I have a responsibility to tell you and Joy."

I hesitated again, looking at Will and Loren. Their attentiveness encouraged me to go on. I took a deep breath and softly released the words, "Clyde has Alzheimer's disease."

I felt as though I had just exploded a bomb in the middle of the room. Although the explosion was inaudible and invisible, it had a profound impact on all of us. In the silence, I turned to look at the backyard through the big floor-to-ceiling windows. I didn't want them to see my tears; I wanted them to have all the space they needed to process their own sorrow.

In the backyard, red flowers danced down from the crape myrtle trees and swirled across the blue water in the swimming pool. The external world felt so irrelevant to the emotional turmoil inside all of us.

I am losing my husband; they are losing their father.

"He was diagnosed last fall, and his memory is getting worse." My eyes followed the flowers floating on the water. In the breeze, they moved without direction, without purpose. "For as long as we have been together, he has been my anchor. I am losing my anchor."

Will broke his silence, his voice low: "He has been your anchor, but he is my root." I turned to look at him and saw his head hanging down. "Jo, I am losing my root." His voice, almost a whisper, choked slightly.

Children of Alzheimer's patients have a set of worries that a spouse may not have. I didn't share Clyde's smart genes, but I didn't share his Alzheimer's genes, either. Early-onset or familial dementia, although less common, has a higher likelihood of being hereditary than dementia that is diagnosed in people over sixty-five. For siblings and children of late-onset dementia patients—diagnosed after the age of sixty-five—on the other hand, the risk of developing Alzheimer's disease is uncertain. Still, given the devastating effects of the disease, that risk becomes a major worry. The familial form of Alzheimer's disease can be positively identified through a genetic test, but most medical professionals have recommended against it for the simple reason that there is little positive outcome from knowing. Despite all the scientific advances that have brought us closer to understanding Alzheimer's disease, we have still found no effective cure.

Will tended to take an intellectual approach to challenges and was also quite intense. The prospect of developing Alzheimer's disease weighed heavily on him.

"Jo, I am scared," Will admitted to me during one of his visits to Dallas. Although our relationship had always been friends rather than mother and son, and although prefixed with *step*, I was still his *mother*, according to age-old tradition accepted in both East and West. It pained me to see him struggle. Yet what could I say to comfort him?

"Will, even if you end up developing Alzheimer's disease later on, don't let it start now. You may never get it at all." I knew my words sounded as trivial as "chicken feathers or garlic skins" (ji mao suan pi, 鸡毛蒜皮), a Chinese expression for something insignificant.

"Loren and I have decided that if either of us develops a terminal illness like Alzheimer's, we will help each other to end the other's life," he said, pensively. "We have each promised not to let the other suffer through that kind of disease." Will was a university IT executive. He had a natural ability to think ahead, to plan rational ways to cope with catastrophe. His statement seemed extreme, but it made perfect sense to me. He and I, a Christian and an agnostic, found that we could agree on many levels.

Will visited often, knowing that his time with his father was limited. He was tremendously supportive of me. Through the years of his father's decline, I witnessed Will's gradual transformation from being an intense and somewhat inflexible person into someone more mature and nurturing. Watching him affectionately put a bite of food into Clyde's mouth and carefully wipe off the excess, I appreciated his protective instinct.

One day Will walked in a different man, or, more precisely, with such a different appearance that he looked unrecognizable: he had a full, shining black beard and looked older, more distinguished, almost mysterious. In fact, he looked like Friedrich Engels, the German socialist philosopher who with Karl Marx cowrote the *Communist Manifesto*, which together with *Quotations from Chairman*, aka *The Little Red Book,* was like a bible in China during the Cultural Revolution in the sixties and seventies. Everyone had to study it. I thought Will looked very cool, so I decided to let Clyde's beard grow. Charlie's cancer treatment had made his hands unsteady; it was better for Clyde to have an unshaven face than a poorly shaven one. And, after all, my husband was not going to deliver a speech at Carnegie Hall anytime soon, or protest my decision.

"Dad would kill you if he knew what you are doing," Joy said to me, chuckling, when she first saw Clyde's unshaven face. Clyde had never been able to stand his face being hairy. The longest he had gone without shaving before then was five days, and that was after much begging and coaxing from me.

"No, he wouldn't, because he would be left without his horsekeeper," I jested with Joy. "Your dad is smarter than that."

Will offered to trim Clyde's beard. He had more skill than I and steadier hands than Charlie. I handed him a pair of scissors and sat by to watch. He moved the scissors around Clyde's face, made small and conservative clips, and sat back from time to time to examine his work. Traditional Anglo-Saxon families of the first half of the twentieth century rarely saw much affection expressed openly between father and son. Such was the culture Clyde grew up in, with an emotionally reserved father. And he had been more or less the same. He had been more awkward showing affection to his son, which had not been the case with his daughter. I might never have witnessed so much physical intimacy between Clyde and Will had it not been for the Alzheimer's disease. Will's tenderness and attentiveness were comforting and seemed natural to me.

Silently, I asked Clyde: *Baby, do you feel your son's love?*

But Clyde was busy carrying on a conversation with the one who was messing around with his face.

Clyde, pointing his right finger into the air: "We were out here, out of here."

Will, working on Clyde's chin: "Out of where?"

Clyde: "I was and I when, and I will be will be . . ."

Will: "Will be what?"

Clyde: "Can you come come talk talk to me?"

Will: "Anything you want to talk about."

Clyde: "We can all just just . . . ?"

Will: "Dad, can you hold it up here?"

Clyde: "It is all good."

Joy, Clyde's daughter, made many visits, sometimes with her two children, sometimes without when the children needed to be in school. Her attitude toward her father's illness, and its possible consequences for her, was straightforward and unflinching. "I didn't want to hide the truth from my children, regardless of how tough this is," she told me. Clyde's grandchildren, watching his gradual decline over the course of several visits, were learning that life is fragile, even as it is robust and resilient. I asked Joy if she was worried about getting Alzheimer's disease and if she wanted to get tested. Her response: "I try not to think about it, and I don't want to know. If it comes, it comes."

I admired her ability to accept and cope. She did not seem afraid of the future. Her strength and understanding allowed me to feel that I didn't always have to be hardcore. I cried on her shoulder on many occasions and never felt I had to hide my vulnerability from her.

During another visit, Joy said to me, "JoAnn, let's all go to a movie with the kids. I know you don't get to go to the movies by yourself. When was the last time you went to one?"

I couldn't recall when I had last watched a movie; it had been a long time. To know that Joy understood my situation and wanted to take care of me moved me profoundly. The ill spouse is the visible victim. Most of the time, conversations, actions, and decisions focus on the needs of the ill, while the needs of the still-able and -agile well spouse remain invisible, neglected and left unfulfilled by the people around as well as by the well spouse. Small acts of kindness, appreciation, and understanding bring much-needed consolation, and something as simple as going to the movies provides a welcome respite from all-consuming care routines.

We left Clyde with Charlie and watched *Hairspray* at the NorthPark mall. Everyone but me knew it was a remake of an old movie. I laughed all the way through and, for a couple of hours, forgot the troubled world of Alzheimer's.

Before Clyde went to Monticello, I found that among the things I did to jog Clyde's memory, nothing worked better than singing, especially old songs and nursery rhymes. Some of those old tunes had fallen out of fashion a long time ago.

We were driving to Lake Ray Hubbard to spend the weekend in our lake house. I was driving, Clyde was in the front passenger seat, and Joy and her two children were in the back.

"Roly Poly," I started cheerily and loudly, then paused to wait for Clyde to continue the song.

"Daddy's little fatty." Predictably, Clyde took the bait and continued in his baritone voice, "Bet he's gonna be a man someday."[54]

The first time I heard Clyde sing this song, he had already been ill. His childhood songs, those he probably hadn't been thinking of for decades, started to come back to him. I thought it was hilarious. It was so out of character to hear such a silly song out of the mouth of my well-educated, culturally sophisticated husband. Apparently, I was not alone. Clyde's singing "Daddy's Little Fatty" amused Joy and her children immensely as well. Neither Joy nor the children had heard this song before. Times had really changed. Referring to someone as a "fatty" had become politically incorrect, a taboo, and a definite no-no. But what could be more energizing and exhilarating for children than to break a taboo! Soon, everyone in the back seat was singing along:

> Roly Poly eatin' corn and taters
> He's hungry every minute of the day
> Roly Poly gnawin' all the biscuit
> As long as he can chew it, it's okay
> . . .
> Roly Poly, daddy's little fatty
> I'll bet he's gonna be a man someday

The melody of "Daddy's Little Fatty" echoed in the lake house for the entire weekend. All the adults grew sick of it, which only fueled the children's enthusiasm.

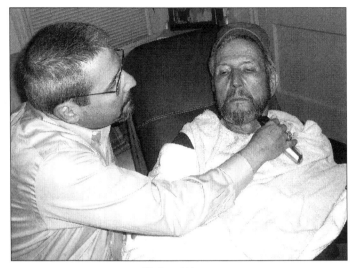

Clyde and his son.

Clyde and his daughter.

Author's son, Stuart, and Clyde's granddaughter, Gabriel,
who is in a red Chinese dress, 2007.

Clyde and Charlie sing together in the big-and-beautiful house.

Thanksgiving 2007. Clyde had been in Monticello for almost two months. The whole Wingfield clan gathered in Dallas: Will, Joy, and their families; Clyde's sister, Georgianna, from Texarkana; his brother, Joe, and his wife, Nada, from Washington, DC; and some of Clyde's nieces and nephews. Also joining us were my son, Stuart; my sister Yun from Shanghai; and, of course, our caregivers and their families.

Charlie and Ronnie picked Clyde up from Monticello and brought him home. Although it was late November, the day was sunny and warm. While guests continued to trickle in, we all sat in the small courtyard, which had never seen so many people before. Clyde was sitting with Charlie, who was holding his hand so he couldn't wander off, and I was in and out of the house, monitoring the progress of the big bird in the oven and preparing other dishes. The guests in the courtyard were debating any number of topics. I remember feeling happy and proud, watching this hodgepodge of family and friends collected on my small patio, among them natural-born as well as naturalized Americans like me; conservatives, liberals, libertarians, and everything in between; devout Christians of different denominations along with agnostics and atheists; urbanites and country folks; people of various skin colors and ethnic backgrounds; and some of this country's more affluent people together with some of the less prosperous. Our group was as diverse as the population of the United States, an epitome of this great nation. We shared views as polarized as night and day and as incompatible as fire and water, but we also shared genuine laughter, eagerly waiting to break bread and attack that big bird together.

The patio door opened, and the conversation came to an abrupt stop. Out onto the patio walked a man slightly taller than me, wearing a warm smile.

Clyde had been sitting quietly with Charlie, unable to follow what people around him were saying and to join in the impassioned nonsense on one side or the other. Now he quickly seized the opportunity to greet the newcomer. He stood up and took a long step toward the guest, offering him his hand and saying, "Hi, I am Clyde Wingfield."

For a fraction of a moment the guest was taken aback, his smile frozen. But he quickly recollected himself. He took Clyde's hand, held it with both of his, and as if they were being introduced to each other for the first time, he responded warmly, "Hi, Clyde, I am Joe." With a slightly awkward chuckle, he added, "I am your brother." It was the same baritone voice as Clyde's: masculine, resonant, familiar, and beautiful, that carried the same type of aura that commanded the entire group's attention. The first time I heard Joe's voice, it was a message he left on the phone for Clyde. I refused to believe it was not Clyde's voice.

Looking at Joe, I could sense the grief behind his smile. How could he not grieve? Joe used to joke that among the three Wingfield siblings, big brother Clyde was the one with brains, able to "talk intelligently on every subject, even the ones he knew absolutely nothing about"; sister Georgianna was the one with looks, who had the attention of all the boys; and poor baby brother Joe had neither. But the poor baby brother Joe, supposedly lacking brainpower and certainly no Cary Grant, had become a successful attorney and married a kind, strikingly beautiful woman of Persian origin, while Clyde, the intellectual one, was struggling with dementia.

With twelve years between them, Clyde and Joe had not been pals as children. In fact, Clyde had told me that Joe's existence became noticeable to him only after he was in the Air Force and returned home to visit when Joe was about eight or nine. But the two Wingfield brothers grew close as adults. Their relationship had been one of deep affection and mutual respect as they both came from the same humble beginning and had become accomplished professionals in their careers. They discovered that they had remarkably similar interests and tastes. They were both avid tennis players, and they had once astonished each other by noticing that they had the same kind of unusual wastebasket in their bathrooms, Joe's in Washington, DC, and Clyde's in Chicago.

It had been about a year since Joe last visited. For family members who hadn't seen the day-by-day changes in Clyde, his condition must have felt drastic and hard to bear. Yet Joe was gracious and patient with his big brother, and Joe certainly had plenty of brain for a quick wit. I was grateful for his unconditional acceptance. No denial, no confusion, no fuss.

Thanksgiving that year was memorable not because of Clyde's deterioration but because everyone shared a good time in spite of Clyde's illness. The Wingfields eagerly devoured three batches of Chinese potsticker dumplings, which almost took the spotlight off that big, fat, twenty-seven-pound bird. I don't like eating fowl and most Chinese don't understand Americans' affinity for turkey, so I was going to cook a small bird as a gesture for Thanksgiving. But Clyde's children insisted on a big bird and promised to finish it up. Finishing up they did, heroically, all except for the bones. My sister Yun taught Clyde's little granddaughter, Gabby, how to do Chinese brush painting, which gained Auntie Yun tremendous affection and admiration from the girl, even though the two of them had no spoken language in common.

Alzheimer's disease robbed me of a wonderful husband, but it brought his family closer to me. They rallied behind Clyde and me in fighting Alzheimer's and eased my acceptance of an agonizing destiny, sharing my grief along the way. They proved to be some of the most decent, intelligent, funny, understanding, appreciative, and down-to-earth "foreign devils." I came to know them very well and felt fortunate to be able to call them my family.

Marcus Tullius Cicero, one of the greatest Roman orators, had this to say about friendship: "What sweetness is left in life, if you take away friendship? Robbing life of friendship is like robbing the world of the sun. A true friend is more to be esteemed than kinfolk." Cicero's words still make perfect sense in the modern world: it is natural that family members often feel more committed to supporting Alzheimer's patients than friends might, simply because of the bonds of kinship. But many of today's families are scattered, sometimes thousands of miles apart, which can make them "the distant water that does not put off a nearby fire (远水救不了近火)," citing a widely used Chinese idiom. Human beings are pack animals. We need people around us to make us feel we belong, and friends often fulfill that need, especially when family are far away.

But how does friendship sustain itself when the friend who is ill doesn't recognize you, doesn't understand your words, doesn't remember your shared past; and, in the middle of your visit, suddenly yells at you, "Get out of my house! Get the hell out!"? What does friendship mean when one of the parties can no longer contribute, interact, or reciprocate? Even close friends may feel uncomfortable or at a loss when around people with Alzheimer's disease. As Alzheimer's patients decline mentally and physically, it is inevitable for both the well spouse and the ill one to lose friends along the way.

A well spouse also faces the challenge of maintaining friendships as the disease progresses. She often feels that she does not belong in social settings. She worries about her ill spouse's inability to interact socially, his feeling left out, his inappropriate behaviors, how other people will perceive him, the awkwardness and disruption he may present, and resentment others may feel toward their presence. Seeing others' joy may be a sad reminder of the well spouse's loss. The list of worries is long, and the emotional sanctuary of friendship is no longer a certainty. As Clyde's disease progressed, I realized that I had to rebuild my emotional sanctuary and nurture my own rose garden, filling it with people who would understand our situation and provide supportive comfort.

Another Wednesday, sunny and bright, a typical spring day in Big D, when the weather seemed to be persistently cheery. Punctually at 11:30, Glen pulled up in front of my house in a big, shiny cream Buick LaCrosse.

"Your friend here." Fong, a caregiver at the time, was feeding Clyde his lunch while watching vigilantly through the window for anything interesting that might happen outside. Dropping the verb "is," like many new immigrants from China whose English hasn't had a chance to catch up, she loudly announced Glen's arrival to me, while I was in the bathroom minding my own business. Fong came to me in summer 2010. She was the third and last Chinese caregiver I had. A woman in her forties from the southernmost Chinese province, Guangdong (Canton), she had big eyes and a dark complexion, typical of a Chinese southerner, with plain black short hair. Her husband, Rob, was a tall, muscular, and handsome bus driver for Dallas Area Rapid Transit (DART). Fong met Rob, who was African American, by responding to his ad for a wife in a Chinese paper, so we teased Fong by calling her a mail-order wife. She didn't mind. She was eager to build her new life in the US, learning English, absorbing new information, and earning an income so she would not be entirely financially dependent on her husband.

Fong went to open the door for Glen. She was fond of him, as was everybody. He was six feet tall and slim with slightly stooped shoulders, gray hair, and a full gray beard. His blue eyes flickered gently behind his glasses, and he always wore a jacket, which made him look like a perfect gentleman, and he was the perfect gentleman "foreign devil." For our regular lunch dates, he always picked me up and made a point of coming inside the house, where he greeted Fong and walked over to Clyde to say hello, never put off by Clyde's consistent lack of response.

Glen and I first met shortly after Clyde's diagnosis, at the farewell party for a friend who had been Clyde's flying partner two decades earlier. I was schmoozing with some people at the party when Clyde came over, pulling a tall fellow by the arm.

"This is my wife, Dr. Lan." Clyde insisted on introducing me with the title of "Dr." whenever professional colleagues were present. He turned to the man. "This is . . . ?"

"Glen," the tall man said. "I heard that you are new here. Welcome to SMU."

Glen was a professor in the engineering department at SMU, as was the guest of honor. Glen and Clyde had been chatting, and he had asked Clyde about his career before retirement. Clyde couldn't remember much. "But my wife can tell you all about it," and he dragged Glen over to me. "Hon, tell him what I did before I retired. You know that better than I do." After our initial encounter, Glen and I did several projects together at SMU. He was, and remains, one of the kindest men I know, a great friend. Sometime later, I learned that his wife, Jean, had been battling Parkinson's disease for a while. There is an old Chinese saying: "Similarly afflicted people take pity on each other" (tong bing xiang lian 同病相怜). In our case, it was our spouses who were similarly afflicted, and we most certainly understood and appreciated each other's struggles. Our friendship grew as our spouses' health declined.

Male well spouses sometimes face different challenges from their female counterparts. Glen, a renowned laser expert, had always been comfortable staying in the ivory tower, pondering complicated ways to make laser beams do marvelous things. Now he found himself struggling with the simple domestic matters his lovely wife had always taken care of during their thirty-year marriage: grocery shopping, cooking, doing laundry, paying bills, and staying involved with the lives of their adult children, who lived in different states and countries. He was surprised when overdue bills piled up and the electric company threatened to cut off service. Glen the breadwinner and brilliant scientist was hardly proficient at changing diapers, feeding, cleaning, managing caregivers, and other things that are more natural for a woman, traditionally speaking. But we understood each other's challenges; we talked to each other without fear of being judged or misunderstood, or burdening our children or others with too much of the unpleasant day-to-day reality we were facing. We consulted with and consoled each other, and confided with each other if we were scared, worried, feeling depressed or deprived, or guilty that we were not able to give our job our 150 percent while giving our ill spouses 100 percent. I even shared my shrink with Glen, referring him to my therapist for depression and anxiety. As far as I was concerned, that was friendship in its highest form. As well spouses, we shared not only our profound sorrow and grief but also our unwavering commitment to caring for our respective ill spouses.

Every well spouse has stories. Some of Glen's stories made me sad, and others made me smile. One I remember fondly was about a day when he was feeding Jean. After the last spoonful of food, he wiped Jean's face with a warm hand towel, making sure to cover all the basics: the corners of her eyes, the sides of her nose, and around her lips. I could picture Glen's tall form bending slightly, his movements somewhat clumsy yet gentle, while Jean, thin and frail, leaned back on the pillows, impassive. Most of the time now, she did not recognize her husband and she seldom spoke.

Her eyes quietly followed Glen for a few moments. Then with a faint, innocent smile, Jean spoke: "I think you are very handsome."

Was she complimenting her husband, or a stranger? It didn't matter. It made Glen sad but happy at the same time to be complimented by the woman he loved, and he could share his sadness and happiness with me. He was not alone.

Glen was a handsome man. More importantly, he was my friend. The life of a well spouse may not be entirely impossible without the encouragement and reassurance of family and friends, but my life as a well spouse was certainly a lot more bearable because of Glen's friendship.

Following Clyde's confirmatory diagnosis at the UT Southwestern Medical Center, I was given a card that read: THE PERSON WITH ME HAS ALZHEIMER'S DISEASE. An Alzheimer's patient may appear normal but act oddly or even offensively in public. The card is a discreet way to alert strangers to the fact that the peculiarity is due to an illness. Being absentminded, though, I hardly ever remembered to carry the card or use it. Clyde's and my encounters with strangers spanned the good, the bad, and the ugly, with the ugliest cases always involving the use of a latrine.

After the incident at the luau in Hawaii when the man had yelled at me for allowing Clyde to go into the men's room because he urinated on the floor, I told Joy, woefully, that although Clyde was still physically healthy and active, I could no longer take him out because of his confusion about using a public restroom.

"Why don't you take him to the women's room?" she suggested. "Most people wouldn't mind. I know I wouldn't."

In the eyes of Chinese people, Westerners are open-minded—maybe too open-minded, in matters of gender propriety. In China, at least during the time I was growing up, there were expectations for how boys and girls should behave according to their clearly defined gender roles: no boys wanted to play rubber band skipping, which was played only by girls, and no girls wanted to play soccer. Clothing should not be too revealing—definitely no cleavage showing, please! My Chinese mind had not allowed me to think in such a deviant way until now: if I didn't want to give up all normal activities, if I didn't want to stop going to places with Clyde, if I didn't want to be confined within the high walls of the big-and-beautiful house, I needed to have the courage to break the gender segregation of public restrooms.

It went fine most of the time. I would stick my head into the women's room and do a quick survey. If it was empty, I would grab Clyde's hand

and in we would march. If there were gentleladies inside, I would say, with an apologetic smile, "My husband has Alzheimer's disease. He cannot use the restroom by himself. Does anyone mind if I bring him in here? I will close the door and not disturb any of you." Most of the time, nobody would voice objection, and I would take that as a unanimous yes. Still, I would take Clyde into the restroom with my head down between my shoulders as if I were a thief, not wanting to be noticed. Even if no one said no, some might have found his presence unpleasant or even disgusting. *Please, Clyde Baby, shhh, don't say anything strange.*

A couple of times we were caught. Big trouble! Once, in Walmart, someone saw us go into the women's room together and dutifully reported us. When I walked out with Clyde, the manager rushed over to intercept us, with the store's security guard in tow. He was agitated, yelling and threatening to call the police on us. I attempted to explain, but his wrath drowned out my words. Exasperated, I also raised my voice and began yelling at him about Alzheimer's and the Americans with Disabilities Act (ADA), why we had to go to the women's room, and why we should be allowed to go into the women's room together. But he wouldn't hear me out, and Clyde absolutely didn't have the look of a typical person qualifying for ADA, and maybe the word *Alzheimer's* meant little to him, if anything, and perhaps he was thinking, "I didn't have to grant that man access into an exclusive sanctuary for women inside my kingdom just because you threw out big words like *Alzheimer's* and *ADA!*"

Clyde couldn't understand why we were yelling at each other or what we were yelling about. He had lost his ability to use a latrine properly but not his instinct to protect his woman, his Hon, from another man's bullying. Sensing that the horse was about to butt heads with the manager and his fearsome-looking, stalwart security guard, I quickly pushed him out of the store before things got more heated, perhaps leaving the manager to think that we were in fact criminals running from the police he had threatened to call.

Another time, we stopped in a homey diner for brunch before going for our Sunday walk in the Dallas Arboretum. After eating, Clyde needed to use the latrine. With the Walmart experience in mind, I approached the manager and politely asked for permission to take Clyde into the women's room, thinking that showing my deference to his authority over the restrooms might grant us legitimate access.

"No," he said, "but you can go into the men's room with him."

He sent one of his male employees to make sure that the men's room was clear of other users, and to stay with us in there to make sure that no funny business would happen. Under his watchful eye, as he held the door closed to stop anyone from coming in, I unzipped my husband's pants, helped him to position himself in front of the urinal, held him steady so he would pee in the right spot, then zipped him back up and washed his hands. Clyde and I walked out of the men's room hand in hand. I held my head high, meeting curious stares from men waiting at the door. I swallowed my humiliation and anger because it was my choice to live life the way I wanted, taking care of my husband in the way I thought best. However, it was hard to stifle my sadness and self-doubt. *Have I failed to protect my husband's dignity?* While Clyde was sheltered by his cluelessness, I was mortified but refused to yield to it. Right or wrong, I wanted to hold on to whatever little normalcy of living I had with my husband.

Such unpleasant incidents were rare, however. More often, we encountered strangers who went out of their way to help us. On one occasion, while I was in a women's room with Clyde, I heard a mother explaining to her young daughter, who was looking at us inquisitively, that the man needed help and the woman was helping him. Yet another time, again in a women's room, a beautiful, well-dressed woman approached me while I was washing Clyde's hands. She told me that her mother had dementia, and she wanted to let me know that seeing us was refreshing and inspiring. Strangers came to our aid in numerous other ways as well. Walking with Clyde in the neighborhood one day, I met a young mother, a stranger, pushing a baby in a carriage, smiling at me as if she wanted to say something.

"Do you know me?" I asked. She shook her head.

"Do you know my husband?"

"I have taken him home several times when he has been lost."

On some walks, Clyde dragged his feet, which he had started doing as his physical strength and coordination deteriorated. He waddled like the ducks whose quacking he used to imitate. We were rambling together, slowly, and I tried to steady him as we moved along. When we reached an intersection, cars stopped, patiently waiting in a long line for us to cross the street as if we were two ducklings separated from their flock. One day after we had walked around Williams Park and crossed the street onto the sidewalk to go home, Clyde's legs suddenly froze, and he seemed unable to move at all. I could not support his weight, so I slowly lowered him to let him collapse on the ground. Some cars pulled over; others passed by, then turned around and came back. Concerned strangers got out of their cars and rushed to our assistance. We managed to get Clyde home safely. Soon after that, we started to use a wheelchair for Clyde, but the kindness of strangers continues to inspire me.

Aside from the Walmart and diner incidents, my attentiveness to Clyde when we were out and about frequently and consistently prompted smiles from strangers, who nodded in acknowledgment, understanding, and encouragement. Throughout my well-spouse journey, our encounters with strangers, as much as our interactions with family and friends, reminded me continually that, in spite of our struggles in the face of ignorance, the world was still a place filled with compassion and benevolence.

Strangers became friends too. During my nine-year journey as a well spouse, my life converged with the lives of many caregivers. Some of them, such as Charlie and Ronnie, became a big part of my world. But all the caregivers who helped us left their footprint in my journey as a well spouse, in more ways than one. And sometimes it had nothing to do with the ill spouse. Life is more and better than just caregiving.

This morning as I was coming down the stairs, I heard Fong talking to Gao, a visiting scholar I sponsored from a Chinese university to come to work at SMU for a year. She was staying with me for the time being until she got her own apartment.

"Look, Gao, I got these *newspapers* for you." Every day, Fong took a bus and then walked about a mile through the neighborhoods from the bus stop to the big-and-beautiful house. "They are *flee*. You *lead* English, I don't. You need to learn. Once you finish, I use for puppies." Fong's English was worse than mine in personal pronouns, tenses, and singular or plural forms, but comprehensible nonetheless. Like most people from her province, because the sound *r* didn't exist in her dialect, she couldn't hear or pronounce it, so she substituted *l*'s for *r*'s, as in *flee* for *free* and *lead* for *read*. And we used old paper as pee pads for the puppies, who were only a few months old.

"Thank you, Fong, for taking care of Gao." I was moved by Fong's devotion to her fellow countrywoman. Gao had arrived a couple of days earlier. Fong's Chinglish amused me, as well as her apparent sense of pride and pleasure as someone who had something to "teach" the newcomer: there was a new kid on the block, giving Fong the opportunity to "show off" instead of always being "showed to."

But I was a little unconvinced about her definition of *flee*.

"Where did you get the paper?" I asked, while walking to the family room and sitting by Clyde, who was already in the big blue chair.

"I *pick* them up from the lawns when I walk here *evelee* morning. People *thew* them on the lawn. They don't want them." That was definitely a non-American definition of *flee*.

"Fong, not all papers are free," I inserted my footnote, "and things on people's lawns are private property that we are not supposed to take."

"Ah, not all?" She was puzzled. "I *pick* from the lawn. They *thew* them out there.

They don't want it." She meant that people threw the paper away.

"Newspapers are delivered that way: throwing on lawns."

"Come look at this." Fong was not entirely convinced. *Surely if they want it, they not thew out on the lawn.*

I walked to the kitchen island where Fong had smoothed out the paper on the counter to show Gao. "I *pick* up these papers *evelee* day," she said, looking at me in anticipation, confident that now I would affirm that she was entitled to the paper, and her "teaching" was legit.

The title of the paper jumped out at me big and bold, *Dallas Morning News*, dated on that very day! It was the number one subscription-based paper in Dallas.

"No, Fong! This paper is not free. People have to pay to get it." My shock was evident, which made Fong somewhat defensive.

"But they were just *thew* on the lawn." Privacy and private property were entirely alien concepts to many Chinese who were new to the capitalist system.

"Yes. But they are not free!"

I prayed that none of my neighbors knew that Fong was a house employee of mine.

Friends and caregivers: Candace, Charlie, Yolanda, and Ronnie, Christmas 2008.

Carry on the journey.

Fifteen

MEEMEE'S STORY

You will never walk alone because I will always be with you.

—ANONYMOUS

M Y NAME IS MEEMEE. My brother is Huanhuan. When we were
six weeks old, the woman we now call Mama adopted us. On the
way home that day, Uncle Ronnie was driving, and Uncle Charlie was
sitting by him in the front seat. Mama was sitting in the back seat holding
both of us.

"Charlie and Ronnie," Mama said solemnly, "I want you both to
witness my testimony."

As she looked at us, her dark brown eyes became ever so tender.
"Meemee and Huanhuan, from this day on, you are my babies and I am
your mother." She stroked us lightly, continuing. "Your daddy's name is
Clyde, and you have a big brother, Stuey. I will always love you, protect
you, and take the best care of you. You are my family."

"What do their names mean?" Uncle Ronnie asked.

"*Mee* (蜜) means 'honey' in Chinese, a common name for girls," Mama explained. "*Huan* (欢) means 'happy.' Chinese people repeat the characters in babies' given names to show affection. Hence, Meemee and Huanhuan."

Mama went on to explain that Meemee was short for *Tian Tian Mee Mee* (甜甜蜜蜜), "Sweet-Sweet-Honey-Honey," while Huanhuan was short for *Huan Huan Xi Xi* (欢欢喜喜), "Happy-Happy-Joy-Joy," words often used together in Chinese to describe a happy and wholesome family.

Mama had always wanted a daughter, and now she had me. She held me tightly to her bosom and told me that I was the most beautiful girl to her. She said some old guy a long time ago named *Proper Marry Me* (Prosper Mérimée) proclaimed, authoritatively, that a woman was beautiful if three things about her were dark: her eyes, her lashes, and her complexion, or something like that.[55] Mama said I met all these criteria: My eyes are as dark as the midnight sky and shaped like almonds, considered by Chinese people to be highly desirable for girls. No need for mascara, as my black lashes extend out three inches, flying upward like the wings of a butterfly. My skin is dark, soft, and as smooth as the finest silk. Mama sometimes ties my hair on top of my head with a red or pink ribbon. Often, when Mama takes Huanhuan and me out for a walk, people stop and compliment her on her pretty babies. Mama's response? "They take after their mother." And she smiles triumphantly.

Mama loved to talk to us because we were the only ones with her in the big-and-beautiful house. Although we often didn't understand what she was saying, we always listened. She told us that 2008 had been an eventful year. For most people, perhaps the most memorable events were the big games held in Beijing in Mama's native country of China, in which only the best athletes, no babies, played, breaking 37 world records and 125 Olympic records; the election of Barack Obama, the first African American president of the United States; and the market crash that made Huanhuan and me worry that Mama wouldn't be able to get us toys and treats. But Mama said not to worry: she bought our toys and treats from a different market, not the one that had crashed, which was the worst since the Great Depression. Phew!

For our mama, the most memorable event of that year was when she brought us to live with her in the big-and-beautiful house. Our big brother, Stuey, had already graduated from university and was working and living on his own. Daddy was living in a small apartment almost next door to us. A few months earlier, Daddy had been booted out of Monticello, a home for people who couldn't live in their own homes, whatever that meant. They said Daddy was wild and a problem at Monticello, because he spat, peed, and cussed everywhere. I hoped that Daddy wouldn't be such a bad boy anymore so that he could live with us in the big-and-beautiful house. But Daddy was still walking around cussing, spitting, peeing, pushing, throwing things, and breaking stuff along the way. Mama couldn't bring him to the big-and-beautiful house to live with us because it was not safe for him or us. Mama was happy to have found a small apartment so close. Uncle Charlie, who loved Daddy very much, was willing to stay with him and care for him.

"Not a perfect solution, but the best one under the circumstances," Mama sighed.

When we were little, real little, Mama sometimes left us in the apartment with Daddy and Uncle Charlie in the morning when she went to work in the office.

"They have eaten their breakfast. Don't feed them," Mama instructed Uncle Charlie, firmly and seriously.

"I won't." Uncle Charlie was always agreeable, especially around Mama, who was the big boss. Uncle Charlie had a sweet voice with a heavy accent. Mama said that was the accent of the Texas Hill Country.

Uncle Charlie would put a bib on Daddy and feed him breakfast as if he were a baby. In those days, Daddy didn't do anything besides eat, sleep, and use the bathroom, and then more eating and sleeping again, all with the help of Uncle Charlie, as if he were a baby. But we knew that our daddy was not a baby. He was our daddy. He had flown airplanes when he was in the Air Force, and he had been in charge of university professors, which was a very hard job. Mama said that before Daddy got sick, he was the smartest man on earth. We couldn't see that, but we took her word for it. Who wants to have a dumb daddy?

We knew Mama was the well spouse to Daddy, who was the ill spouse, and that he needed help to get through the day. Uncle Charlie took care of Daddy along with Mama. He fed Daddy breakfast: oatmeal, Cheerios, yogurt with applesauce, toast with peanut butter, or biscuits and scrambled eggs. Sometimes there were slices of bacon, too. After Mama left, a piece of toast or bacon would *accidentally* drop on the floor, and we knew it was our responsibility to clean it up.

"Uncle Charlie will get in trouble now," Uncle Charlie's sweet Texas Hill Country accent would sound, and a chunk of biscuit would *accidentally* fall down, although we would always have hoped for another piece of bacon.

After he fed Daddy, Uncle Charlie cleaned up the tray, wiped the grease and crumbs off Daddy's mouth and hands, and helped Daddy use the bathroom. Often there were scuffles, because Daddy resisted and resisted using the bathroom. Sometimes there were bathroom accidents for Uncle Charlie to clean up. Afterward it was time to sit down on the couch. Uncle Charlie helped Daddy sit down, then picked us up and put us on the couch by Daddy. We were so little that we were not able to climb up by ourselves yet. Daddy snored rhythmically beside us, and Uncle Charlie hummed a sweet, melancholy country tune somewhere in the back of the apartment, softly reassuring us of our safe place in the world:

> Shannon is gone, I hope she's drifting out to sea
> She always loved to swim away
> Maybe she'll find an island with a shady tree
> Just like the one in our backyard[56]

It was a song about the death of a beloved dog of the same name, we were told.

With our bellies full and the couch warm and soft underneath us, all three of us soon drifted off to dreamland. I woke up to the smell of lunch simmering on the stove. *Meatloaf? No, chicken and dumplings!* Comfort food was the specialty of Uncle Charlie the chef. Then I heard Mama tiptoeing over to the couch. I thought she was going to pick me up, since I was her princess. "Ladies first," she often told Brother Huanhuan, which meant I ate first and got picked up by Mama before him. Instead, she sat down between us and Daddy, who was still sound asleep, snoring loudly, a tiny stream of saliva hanging from the corner of his mouth. Mama pulled a piece of tissue from the box on the coffee table and dabbed lightly to dry his mouth and cheek. She started to stroke Daddy's face, so gently, and his hair, so gently. Then she reached over and kissed Daddy's eyes, even more gently, and played with Daddy's eyelashes with her lips. It made me jealous, so I started to whine a little.

Mama smiled. She turned to us and picked us up, both of us. She caressed us and kissed us on our heads too, and then settled us on her lap. That was so awesome!

The commotion woke up Daddy. He saw Mama and smiled. Daddy never failed to smile when he saw Mama's face.

"Hi, Sleeping Beauty. I am Lan Jiang. I am your wife. I am here." Mama liked to remind him who she was whenever she was with him.

"Lan *Chiang*." Daddy said Mama's Chinese name with a foreign accent. He didn't talk much, just uttered a few words and sometimes a phrase here and there. Hardly any clear sentences, though. He slowly raised his hand to touch Mama's face, as if he needed to feel certain that it was Mama next to him. Mama moved her face to meet Daddy's unsteady hand. She knew he needed the reassurance of her presence. "Lan Jiang." Daddy repeated the name, more clearly and confidently this time. Daddy was the only non-Chinese person who called Mama by her Chinese name, the name she had used when they first met. Throughout the day, whether Mama was away from him, or somewhere nearby, or sitting right by him holding his hands and looking into his eyes, Daddy called out Mama's name tirelessly. He kept her deep in his consciousness, but he seldom recognized her now.

"Yes, I am Lan Jiang. I am your wife. I am here."

"You know you know all of them both ways?" Daddy asked.

Mama smiled but didn't say anything.

"You don't know who I am I am, do you?" He asked another question.

"I know who you are—do you know who I am?" Mama was apparently amused.

"I love you very much." Daddy avoided answering the question.

"I love you very much, too. Can we get married, then?" Mama teased Daddy.

Daddy went silent, as if to figure out what that meant.

"I promise you a very good dowry. Will you marry me?" Mama teased Daddy some more.

Our mama was our daddy's guardian and protector, and he was her baby, just like Huanhuan and me. Mama told us that for over a decade, she had been his Queen of Hearts and partner in crime, while he had been her knight in shining armor, her constant guide on the side, and her anchor in life, whatever that meant. "Such is the alteration of roles of a well spouse," said Mama, shaking her head slightly.

Daddy's unfocused eyes started to focus on Mama's face, and he smiled again. Mama put one of her hands on Daddy's hand while leaving her other hand on us to stop us from whining. I felt content.

"Do you want to feed Clyde?" Uncle Charlie came into the room with a bowl of steaming hot chicken and dumplings, announcing that lunch was ready, and he put a bib on Daddy as if he were a baby. He knew that Mama loved to feed Daddy. Just as she insisted on bathing and grooming us herself, feeding and grooming Daddy were activities she considered essential for maintaining intimacy with those of us she loved so much, especially in the absence of most verbal communication. Whenever she clipped our nails—Daddy's, Huanhuan's, and mine, fifty-eight pieces all together since I have just four toes in each of my back legs—she would say, "This keeps us connected."

When Mama fed Daddy, she first tested the temperature of the food with her lips and blew on it carefully, making sure the spoon had just the right amount in it, not too little, not too much. Mama said that Daddy used to be an elegant eater. We couldn't see that, but we took her word for it. Daddy certainly did not eat elegantly these days. He stuck his fingers into the bowl of chicken and dumplings and tried to pick up the gooey food to put into his mouth. Sometimes he bit his own finger and cried out in pain. Bits of gooey food dropped on the tray in front of him, stuck on his face, and hung from his beard, making him look funny. Mama gave him a spoon to keep his hand occupied so he wouldn't play with his food. He put the spoon in his mouth and tried to bite it, or struck it on the tray to make annoying noises. Unlike when Uncle Charlie fed Daddy, there was no chance that any food would drop on the floor when Mama was feeding him. We women are just way neater than men, and Mama was definitely neater than Uncle Charlie!

Mama spent most of her time in her office at the university, doing an important job. After she finished work, she would stop briefly at the big-and-beautiful house to change and to pack us up to go see Daddy. We stayed there until Daddy went to bed. Mama and Daddy had built the big-and-beautiful house after Daddy became ill because it was very close to her office. Even though it was new and modern, coming home to the empty house hadn't made Mama happy since Daddy had moved out. Then one day, a few months after Mama brought us to live with her in the big-and-beautiful house, she came in with a heartfelt smile on her face, though her eyes were glittering with tears.

Meemee, the little lady.

"I haven't felt such happiness in coming home since your daddy left. The thought of someone at home waiting for me and being very happy to see me is something I haven't had for a long time." She picked up Huanhuan and me and kissed each of us on the forehead, whispering, "Babies, you have made coming home meaningful again."

That made me so happy. We were always ecstatic to see Mama come home. We always made sure that she knew how thrilled we were by dancing around, wiggling our tails, and giving her plenty of puppy kisses.

Huanhuan, the first mate, Lake Ray Hubbard, Rowlett, Texas.

Sixteen

HUANHUAN'S STORY

Who deserves a hero's trophy as we face each catastrophe?
Nobody else but you.

—GOOFY, in A Goofy Movie

M*ama is coming! Mama is here!!*
Even before I saw the shadow of her slim figure on the opaque glass of the front door, I recognized her footsteps: one foot landing more heavily than the other, pounding hastily on the paved path. Now she was fumbling for the key. *Hurry! Hurry!!* My sister, Meemee, and I waited right inside the front door, with bated breath and wagging tails, in anticipation. Now the key turned. *Click.* The door opened, and in came our dear mama!

Oh, joy! We stood up on our hind legs, dancing with elation and wiggling with excitement. I even did a somersault. *Oh, joy!* So happy that Mama was home!

Mama smiled. She patted us on the back and gently scratched our necks behind our ears, in the spot that felt so good. I lay down and flipped my belly up for a little belly rub. But she gave my belly only a quick smooch, then picked up Meemee and started walking toward the family room in the back of the house, next to the kitchen.

Why didn't she pick me up? Boys need a little TLC, too!

I followed Mama straight to the family room, where Daddy's hospital bed took up the entire west wall. She bent over Daddy's face. With a smile, she spoke loudly and deliberately into his ear, just as she did every day.

"Hi, Baby, I am home. I am Lan Jiang. I am your wife." Daddy responded with some faint murmuring.

"I love you, Baby," Mama continued. She believed that in his deepest, most primal consciousness, Daddy could still feel her love for him.

Slowly and tentatively, Daddy extended his arms out to touch Mama's face, as if trying to identify her with his hands. Mama took his hands in hers, pressed them against her face, and rubbed and kissed them tenderly. She touched his face gently, smoothed his fine salt-and-pepper hair, and tested his forehead to make sure his temperature felt normal. Next, she reached underneath him to check his disposable briefs.

Mm-hmm! Wet. After some maneuvering, she managed to replace the wet ones with a fresh pair.

When we were adopted in fall 2008, Daddy was living two doors down with Uncle Charlie and Uncle Ronnie. In summer 2009, after Uncle Charlie got very ill and Daddy no longer walked, Mama moved Daddy back to the big-and-beautiful house to live with all of us so she could take care of Daddy in the night. Mama said when she had to send Daddy away from home, never in her mind could she have imagined Daddy would someday circle his way back home again. We were all so happy to be together.

Hi, my name is Huanhuan (欢欢). It means "happy" in Chinese. I was the last born, the smallest and weakest in a litter of five that included my sister, Meemee. Coming from the same parents, a black shih tzu mother and a white poodle father, we are, naturally, black and white, though in different ways. Meemee is all black except for her white chest, white paws, and a bit of white on the tip of her tail. I am pearly white with a few strategically placed black spots. I am also now much bigger and, I think, more of a head-turner than Meemee, which makes her very jealous.

"Salt and pepper," a passerby commented.

"Yin and yang," Mama responded, which was very Chinese of her.

Our current mama adopted Meemee and me in 2008, six weeks after we were born and six years after our daddy got ill. Mama said that when I was born, I was so small that I could hardly get to my mother's milk. Our keeper at the time had to pick me up and place me at my biological mother's belly so I could get fed. When I was little, Mama paid extra attention to me, since I was the weaker of the two. Maybe that is why I developed an Oedipus complex. I never took my eyes away from my mama. I followed her tirelessly upstairs, downstairs, to the living room, to the kitchen, upstairs again, downstairs again, and then all the way into the bathroom. I anticipated her every movement and got it right most of the time: upstairs to write a check for Uncle Charlie and downstairs to leave it on the kitchen counter for him; back upstairs to get more care supplies from storage, downstairs again to put them in Daddy's room; then to the kitchen to fill the baby cup with apple juice for Daddy; and now at his bedside, putting his arms on her shoulders and carrying him to the portable stool, then taking him back to bed. Then, finally, back upstairs for the night. In the middle of the night, there was always a trip downstairs to check on Daddy. During that trip, I stood at the top of the stairs, listening intently to Mama's every move, preparing to dash down to her aid if some monster emerged from the darkness outside.

I am very anxious about being separated from Mama. Uncle Charlie and Uncle Ronnie teased me for being gender confused. "Huanhuan must be a gay boy because he is such a sissy. Most gay men are mama's boys." They were both experts on the subject, being both a gay couple who had been together for the past decade, and each extremely attached to, adored by, and adoring of their respective mamas. Also, Mama had made sure that we were neutered and spayed, so maybe I have no gender.

Every cell of my canine being is devoted to my mama.

Daddy, though, was the reason Mama adopted us. As Daddy's Alzheimer's disease progressed, his ability to communicate diminished rapidly. Mama felt very lonely without Daddy to talk to. She missed the daddy who was eloquent, knowledgeable, engaging, humorous, and full of stories; the man who had always listened to her attentively and patiently, making her feel respected, understood, and encouraged. Even I, a lowly canine, understand the importance of communication to one's sense of belonging and happiness. Meemee and I communicate by woofing, wiggling, sniffing, licking, and sometimes howling and gnawing, which of course are behaviors Mama disapproves of.

There were horror stories about hanging and eating dogs during Mama's younger years in the Gobi Desert in China. During the late 1960s and early 1970s, when the relationship between the governments of China and the Soviet Union went sour, the Chinese government ordered that all dogs be slain in the village where Mama was living, for fear that their barking would expose troop movements on the border. Food was scarce, so nothing went to waste. The villagers hanged their beloved dogs, shed some tears, and then ate the dog meat. Such stories gave me nightmares.

The author and a friend in front of their "cave" home in Inner Mongolia.

Mama, however, loves animals. She never passes a dog without asking to pat it. She talks to ducks, calling them her "web-footed friends," and she used to feed the mama duck who nested on our lawn. She rescued a turtle from her Chinese friend before it had been served on a dinner plate. She named it Orie, short for Oracle, referring to ancient Chinese characters carved on tortoise shells that were used for divination. When we chased squirrels, she scolded us, threatening to whip our butts.

As for us canines, who could be better companions? We are loyal, intuitive, playful, cute, and eager to please; at least I am, though my sister is more like a feline than a canine. She is an independent woman like Mama.

America's best storyteller, Mark Twain, once said, "Heaven goes by favor. If it went by merit you would stay out and the dog would go in."[57] He was right. We have helped Mama cope with the stress and loneliness of being a well spouse, and we have made her laugh. She is a strong woman already, but she has told us that our unconditional love has made her even stronger.

In the early days, when we were tiny babies, Mama sometimes put us on the tray of the big blue chair that Daddy sat in all day. He had no clue who we were. Seeing us wiggling around on the tray in front of him, he chuckled as if he were tickled. That made Mama smile. I love to make Mama smile.

Daddy might not have had any clue who we were, or who anybody was, but, like a newborn baby, his eyes were attracted to anything that moved. On the tray in front of him, we rolled around like two little fur balls, one white, one black; or, as Mama described us, like "two crawling rats." We would catch Daddy's attention. Slowly and unsteadily, Daddy would extend one hand over me and squeeze me tentatively, gently at first, and then harder. When his squeeze got so hard it hurt, I would screech. One time, Daddy grabbed me firmly from the back, picked me up, and brought me to his mouth. Next thing I knew, he was nibbling at my nose. I screamed at the top of my lungs, though I was more scared than hurt. Mama rushed to my rescue. It took her some maneuvering to free me from Daddy's mighty grip. His hands, unlike some other parts of his body, had not gone a bit feeble.

"These are your children," Mama said, caressing Daddy's hand as if to apologize for her harsh actions as she worked to pry his hand open. "You are not supposed to eat your children." I was disappointed that her tone was so tender when my life had been in serious danger just a moment before!

But we also had fun sitting with Daddy on his big old chair. After he had finished eating, there were often a few Cheerios or bits of cheese, pancakes, and our favorite—bacon—for us to nibble on. Sometimes we ventured off the tray and climbed up Daddy's chest. We gave him kisses, which was the only way we knew to show him our affection. Daddy chuckled—he must have thought it was funny—and kissed us back. Encouraged by his response, Meemee and I kissed him with even more enthusiasm. But Mama took us away. She said Daddy didn't like that, but we were not so sure.

Daddy was no longer able to walk, but his hands sure kept busy. He grabbed everything within reach and wouldn't let go of anything that he had captured. It seemed as though all the energy he saved by not walking got channeled to his hands. Whatever he grabbed, he put into his mouth and tried to bite it. Mama said that he was regressed to what that esteemed shrink Sigmund *Fraud* (Freud) called the *oral stage*, during which a baby's main source of interaction with the world occurs through the mouth. It certainly was not true in our case. We canine babies experience the world through our nose, by sniffing and touching, a much safer way, I believe. The harder the object, the harder and more determinedly Daddy bit. He would bite a spoon or fork, then use it to stab the tray as if he were mad at the utensil for refusing to surrender to his teeth. After chewing on a piece of paper or a washcloth, he would tear it in pieces and scatter them on the floor or throw them into a corner.

Meemee and I tried to help clean up Daddy's messes. When Mama or Uncle Charlie put some crackers or slices of bread on the tray, Daddy would eat them up, and then Meemee and I would clean up the crumbs. If they gave him Cheerios, some fell into his mouth, but most fell on the floor. Meemee and I cleaned those up, too. Once Mama put a pacifier on the tray so he could chew on something harmless, but it made him gag, so Mama took it away.

We got tickled and scratched not only by Mama, Uncle Charlie, and Uncle Ronnie, but also by visitors who came and went like schools of fish: hospice nurses, hospice doctors, Mama's friends, big brother Stuey and his friends, and other family members. Since attempts to converse with Daddy were impossible, everyone resorted to singing our praises instead. "How cute they are!" "So well behaved!" "Adorable!"

The hospice nurses came to visit almost every day. They checked Daddy's vital signs, looked at his skin for bedsores, measured his arm for weight loss, and asked about his appetite, to which the answer was always that it was good. They also asked if he was regular. Of course Daddy was not regular. Even we little ones knew he was not regular. Our daddy was ill. A regular daddy would be working, helping Mama with the household chores, and taking care of us. We needed to be walked, fed, groomed, and bathed, and we needed to be held and loved. Also, a regular daddy would be able to bathe and use the toilet by himself. Our daddy sat all day long and let Mama, Uncle Charlie, and others take care of him.

Why did the nurse ask if our daddy was regular when it was so obvious that he was not? Even Meemee, who is usually slow to catch on to everything except stuff that has to do with eating, understood that our daddy was not regular. To the nurse's question of whether Daddy was regular, Uncle Charlie's response was often that Daddy was "constipated." Meemee, of course, wanted to know what *constipated* meant. I had to tell her in the plainest, simplest language so she could understand: "Daddy can't poop."

"Ew, gross! Mama doesn't like it when you speak so crudely." Meemee now thought that she was a lady because Mama always said she was a little lady. But it wasn't my fault that I had to deal with so much ignorance.

I was glad of the opportunity to feel a little superior to Meemee. It was not easy for me to compete with that feisty, domineering young lady. I know it is a cliché, but it is true: life is not fair. When Mama tells me, "Ladies first, Huanhuan. Be a gentleman," I know that means Meemee eats first, Mama picks her up first, she sits on the puffiest feather pillow during the day, and she sleeps on the softest spot on the bed at night, burying her slim little body deep in a quilt filled with the most downy goose down covered in the most lustrous silk. Mama expects me to be a gentleman like my daddy. I want to please my mama more than anything, so I accept the fact that being a gentleman means I will always be second to Meemee in the house.

And I am afraid of Meemee anyway, although she is only two-thirds my size. Anytime I get too close to her food bowl, or try to get Mama's affection, or stretch a little too close to where she is resting, or move around her in a way that isn't to her liking, she never hesitates to snarl at me and show me those nasty little teeth of hers. It is beyond my comprehension why Auntie Yun calls Meemee's teeth "pretty little sweet rice grains." To me, there is nothing pretty or sweet about them.

A typical winter day in Dallas—windy, wet, dark, and cold. Mama looked out the window. Bare trees quivered in the wind, and the world was in dull gray and black. She was reluctant to go out for a walk.

"It's too cold." Holding our leashes, she looked at us as if she were talking to us, but we knew she was debating with herself. "And it's too wet."

But we didn't really mind the weather. We have fur coats. Plus, we had a wardrobe that included padded jackets, sweatshirts, windbreakers, and raincoats. We loved walking in the neighborhood or running free on the manicured grounds of Southern Methodist University, where Mama worked. We begged with our eyes and tails, *Please! Please!!* We knew her soft heart could not resist our dogged pleas. With an ambivalent sigh, she wrapped Daddy up in thick blankets, put his hands in a pair of leather gloves, and covered his head with a wool cap. She strapped Daddy's feet onto the footrests of the wheelchair with some Velcro so he couldn't keep taking his feet off the footrests and sticking them on the ground. She also strapped Daddy's hands to the armrests because he kept putting them on the moving wheels. Finally, out into the winter chill we went.

Fortunately, Dallas's winters are short. Soon spring returned, then summer. When the sky outside began to brighten, our outings became regular again. On the day of our last outing with Daddy, he was wearing a bright red cap with an unusually long bill. He looked like a raven. Mama had bought that cap in Hangzhou, a beautiful city in China an hour from Mama's hometown, Shanghai, on a trip she had taken with him when she was invited to give lectures at a university there. Daddy was already ill and had a tendency of wandering off in crowds in China following some stranger he thought was Mama. With this hat, Mama could easily spot him in the crowd.

Mama pushed the wheelchair and Auntie Yun, who was visiting from China, held our leashes. As usual, we made a stop at Starbucks. Mama and

Auntie got steaming hot lattes, an oatmeal raisin cookie, and a croissant. We sat at the picnic table in the park by the red brick house that was University Park's city hall, bathing in the early summer sun. Mama split the cookie and croissant between Auntie and herself. She fed a little to Daddy, who opened his mouth at the touch to his lips, like a nestling bird waiting to be fed; then she placed a small piece of croissant in front of Meemee, and then one for me. "Ladies first," she said. "Huanhuan, you are a gentleman like your daddy."

Well, do I have a choice?

At the picnic table next to us, a young mother was sitting with a small boy and a baby, who was in a stroller. When the toddler came over to pat us, his mom commented to Mama how well we were behaving. "Yes. Their mama has made sure that they have gotten a good education," Mama said. "Both of them have diplomas."

Yes, we do, from PetSmart!

The young mother's eyes lingered on Daddy, inquisitively. She paused for a moment, then carefully said, "I see you and your husband a lot in the neighborhood. May I ask what has happened to him?"

"It's quite all right to ask." Mama never wanted to avoid the truth. "Clyde has had Alzheimer's disease for years now." She added, calmly, "He was a very intelligent man and a wonderful husband." An expression of sympathy hung over the young mother's face. Mama went on to tell her that they had a good relationship and that she had a strong support system. She refused to let people think of her as a victim.

The smell of freshly cut grass was irresistible. For just a few minutes, Mama unleashed us. Off we ran, like stones released from a slingshot, chasing squirrels and chipmunks, ducks and geese, rabbits and rats, and each other. Our ears were flapping, tails fluttering, and long hair flying. We were two fur balls, one black and one white, scudding across the manicured lawn.

"They are so cute," passersby commented.

"Yes, they take after their mama," Mama replied, showing no humility, her eyes flickering with a mischievous smile, waiting for people to laugh.

And laugh they did, always. Mama laughed with them, the kind of heartfelt laughter that could save the day of a well spouse.

Daddy passed away on September 15, 2011. We were two years old. I knew something serious had happened because two big guys in black suits, starched and neatly pressed white shirts, and white gloves came to the house in the middle of the night. Their grave expressions made it clear to me that they were not here for a fancy black-and-white cocktail party. They carried Daddy away from his bed on a stretcher. Mama, who usually greeted everyone with warm smiles, didn't smile at all. The next day, there was no more speaking loudly to Daddy. Instead, Mama sat in complete silence by Daddy's empty bed, staring at nothing. Meemee and I went to sit with her. We leaned our small, warm bodies against her lonely and rigid figure. Quietly, we looked up into her dark brown eyes, and we knew that she knew that we knew, and we knew that she knew that we cared, and we knew that she knew that we would always be by her side, for better or for worse.

That night, on the bed in which we all slept, she buried her face in my fur coat. Tears soaked my fur coat wet.

Waiting for Mama's cue.

The author in her peasant years in Inner Mongolia during the Cultural Revolution.

Seventeen

BETTER ANGELS

Of course, when I say human nature is gentleness,
it is not one hundred percent so.

—THE DALAI LAMA

IN THE EPIC WAR FILM *Apocalypse Now*, Lieutenant General Corman says to Captain Willard, "Well, you see, Willard, in this war, things get confused out there. . . . because there's a conflict in every human heart, between the rational and the irrational, between good and evil, and good does not always triumph. Sometimes, the dark side overcomes what Lincoln called the better angels of our nature."[58]

Corman is talking about how soldiers behave in war, a far more intense context in which to weigh the rational and irrational, or good and evil, than what we experience in ordinary times, but the idea that the better angels of our nature do not always prevail applies to all humans. As Corman indicates, everybody has a "breaking point."

An event that drove me to maddening rage did not occur during my years as a well spouse but in the fanatical pinnacle phase of the Cultural

Revolution in China. One December night in 1967, a few weeks after my fourteenth birthday, ferocious pounding on the door of our home in the quiet former French concession of Shanghai erupted at about one o'clock in the morning, violently breaking the stillness of the night and waking everyone inside. A gang of about ten people, the so-called Revolutionary Rebels, barged in. My siblings and I were on our own; Mom and Dad had already been taken away, confined somewhere, separated from each other, barred from communicating with any of us children, and they were subjected to both psychological humiliation and physical abuse.

The intruders ordered all five of us, ages sixteen, fifteen, fourteen, twelve, and ten, out of bed. They rounded us up in Dad's study and demanded that we denounce our parents. Leading the group was a college-educated young man perhaps in his upper twenties who had once been my father's bright and faithful protégé. My father had mentored

The author (left) with her sister Yun in the late 1970s.

him with much kindness, and he had seemed like an older brother to us until Dad was stripped of his party position in Shanghai's government.

"Is your dad a good person or a bad person?" The young "leader" was eager to prove his "revolutionary standing" to his comrades by vilifying his former boss. Dad had been accused of being a revisionist and a capitalist roader, whatever that meant.

Without hesitation, my sister, the oldest among us, answered firmly, "Dad is a good person. He wants us to serve our country."

"You don't know your dad." His tone was bold and commanding, his former gently deferential manner all gone. "He has disguised himself very well."

"Dad is an honest person. He is loyal to the party." My sister bravely stood fast.

"You are young and naïve. Your dad has fooled you all. You must choose to draw a clear line between him and yourselves, or you'll be knocked down by the revolutionary masses!" Softening his tone somewhat, he cajoled us defenseless children: "Think carefully and be smart. You don't want to oppose the revolutionary masses."

While a few of them continued to interrogate us, grilling us about the groundless claim that my parents had said and done things to slander the great leader Chairman Mao and the Communist Party of China, others savagely looted the house, throwing things out of drawers and turning the beds upside down, searching for nonexistent evidence to prove that my parents had betrayed the party. The temperature outside had fallen below freezing, but no home in Shanghai was heated in those days. We were all in our sleeping garments. I sensed that behind his thick glasses, the eyes of my father's former protégé had become those of a predator fixing on its prey, greedily penetrating the thin layer of fabric to linger on my undernourished and undeveloped body. I was trembling, not due to the cold, which I hardly noticed, or out of fear—that had passed after the initial shock—but because of my growing rage and desperation. These people had already taken my beloved parents away and treated them harshly; now they had ruthlessly invaded my home and ripped away my safe haven, threatening my siblings and me. I clenched my teeth in bitter hatred, and my mind went frantic and deranged, struggling to control the violent urge inside me to destroy those who were trying to destroy me with their assaults on everything I had lived for.

Kill! Kill them! KILL THEM ALL! The knives are in the kitchen, whatever may happen! I can't take it anymore. Let me perish with them! I must stop this ordeal!

In Shakespeare's *King Lear*, the Fool declares, "This cold night will turn us all to fools and madmen." Mao's Cultural Revolution had turned the whole of China manic.

Forty years later I was older and wiser, and my once-in-a-lifetime killing instinct was all but extinct. However, during my decade-long experience with what Nancy L. Mace calls "the 36-hour day" in her book of the same name on caring for people with Alzheimer's disease,[4] the better angels of my nature were tested, again and again, sometimes beyond my capacity, and sometimes the good did not prevail.

By the end of 2004, two years after Clyde's diagnosis, it was apparent that Clyde was increasingly in need of assistance. We purchased a duplex house that was being built in University Park just half a mile from my office, on the same crape-myrtle-lined street. No more rush-hour traffic to fight, no more worries about the danger of the swimming pool, and I could check on Clyde during my lunch hour every day.

After agonizing delays, cost overruns, and countless hours of my time, the house was finally finished. I was quite pleased with the results. The light gray sandstone façade held a hint of French blue. The black wrought iron gate corresponded with the wrought iron frame around the arched top and heavy frosted glass of the front door. At night, a light over the door shone on the entryway, and wall sconces illuminated the side path. French doors in the family room opened onto a small private courtyard, bringing in cool breezes on warm days; a Carrara marble–encased fireplace radiated warmth on cold nights. I had sifted through hundreds of granite slabs from all over the world to pick out the kitchen countertop. In sweeping strokes of various shapes, nature had painted on the granite a Chinese splash-ink landscape in shades of green, gray, and brown, suggesting streams flowing down a stony riverbed. The walls in the sunny half of the house were painted a soft sage called Queen Anne's lace, while for the shady side I had chosen a cheerful yellow fittingly named Sunnyside. A long hallway connected the four bedrooms on the second floor. Those at either end had French doors with black wrought iron balconettes in a swirling pattern that reminded me of passionate Spanish dances. Throughout the interior's 3,300 square feet were tall ceilings, intricate crown moldings, textured walls, hand-scraped wood and Travertine floors, European-style chandeliers and sconces, and heavy silk draperies. I intended the house to be a classy French country home in the heart of the cowboy land.

When I designed the house, I bore in mind that Clyde would soon no longer be able to travel; I wanted to provide plenty of space for his children and grandchildren to come and visit. We eventually referred to the house as the "big-and-beautiful house" to distinguish it from the other places where Clyde stayed later, such as Monticello and the small apartment down the street.

In the house on Ranchita Drive in North Dallas, the moving company had been packing for days. On a cold December morning in 2005, the crew came punctually at eight o'clock with their massive truck. The owner of the company was a deft and delightful Hispanic woman whose English was impressively fluent with just a touch of accent. She reassured me that the move would be done by midafternoon and left her crew with me to do their deed. But as the afternoon wore on, it became apparent that we were nowhere near the finish line.

The Ranchita home was finally empty after nightfall. We had to unload the truck in the dark at the new house. Inside, much still needed to be done: unpacking, reassembling and positioning furniture, and removing piles of packing material. At about eight thirty, the boss lady appeared with her five children in tow, aged two to seventeen. The little one stayed in her arms, and she ordered the older ones to join the crew. They threw themselves into the job, bolstered by music and by the soda and pizza I had ordered for them. The happy team worked energetically to finish, having committed to another job the following day.

I had designated Wang, our competent and opinionated Chinese caregiver at the time, to watch Clyde so that I could deal with the moving process. (Charlie and Ronnie had yet to enter our lives.) As night fell, the temperature dropped. There was no warm and quiet place at the new house for Wang to park Clyde: the doors stayed open for the comings and goings of the movers, there was commotion everywhere, and the house was in total disarray. Wang dressed Clyde in my long down coat, which looked feminine and was too tight for him. His big nose dripped from the cold like a slowly leaking hundred-year-old faucet. Wang had to wipe it constantly, and she was having trouble keeping him away from me.

"Hon, I am cold. Take me home." Standing outside the house where

I was helping unload, Clyde grabbed my sleeves, sniffling and shivering, refusing to go inside.

We managed to find a beach towel to wrap around him. Now he looked pathetic, like a refugee from a faraway famished and war-stricken land.

"Baby, you go inside. I have to finish this." I had no time for him.

"Hon, I want to go. I am hungry." It was after ten o'clock, more than four hours since he had eaten supper.

Wang microwaved a piece of pizza for him. He didn't touch it, but she was able to get him to sip some hot tea.

"Hon, let's go. I am tired."

"Hon, I think I am sick. I have a headache." We searched and dug out an Excedrin for him.

"Hon, let these people handle it. I want to go home." He hovered right by me persistently, as sticky as a piece of chewed-on chewing gum on my sole.

Finally, by midnight, the crew had finished. As planned, I put my sniffling and shivering, fatigued and frustrated, confused and complaining, pathetic-looking husband in the car. Dragging my own dog-tired body behind the steering wheel, I drove east toward our lake house, about twenty miles from Dallas, toward warmth, a soft clean bed, order and serenity, and a chance to relax.

"Just another half hour, Baby, and we will be there." I was stretched very thin, so thin that I was worried that one more push would break me into pieces.

Please, Baby, no more pestering.

As soon as the car started moving, the conversation began to go nowhere.

"Hon, where are we going? I want to go home."

"Yes, Baby, we are going home now."

"But shouldn't we be going that way? Where are we going?"

"We are going the right way. Please trust me. We will be home soon. I will get you a hot bath. I know you are cold." I was trying my best to avoid an infinitely looping dialogue, but my frustration was increasing.

"But home is that way, I am sure."

"Baby, I don't know what is 'that way.' We are going home!" I raised my voice, hoping my words would register with him.

"I am cold, and I am so tired." His voice was truly pitiful. It reminded me how vulnerable he was and how hard it must have been for him to have had such a long and strenuous day without understanding what was going on.

"I know. I am sorry. I didn't know it would take so long." I put my hand on his leg and gave it a gentle squeeze. It was my nonverbal way of telling him, "I understand, Baby."

But he didn't take my cue. He was getting more persistent. "Hon, you are not hearing me! I want to go home."

"We *are* going home. Please understand!"

The thought that he was going to persistently harass me all the way with the same question and that I would have no way to stop him made me feel hopeless and helpless. I grew increasingly tense and anxious.

"Hon, let's turn around. I cannot do this anymore." Clyde was getting more persistent and feeling increasingly desperate as well.

"Can you please *understand* that we *are* going home? Can you please *stop* repeating yourself?" I could no longer conceal my irritation. "Let me focus on driving."

"I don't know where you are going! Why are you doing this? Please take me home." His mind pursued his own thoughts, refusing to hear me or to acknowledge that I was upset and that I was *right*.

"We are going home! *We are* going home! Why can't you hear me? Why don't you understand? *We-are-going-home!* I don't know where you want to go! I can't go where you want to go. *You don't know where you want to go!* If you know, take us there! Stop bugging me, stop repeating! You are driving me insane!"

I was yelling, unable to stop my anger. This long, hard day had depleted my patience and short-circuited my temper, and not being able to stop Clyde's perseveration and his persistent undeliverable demands was making me mad.

Clyde hadn't expected my sudden tantrum. For a moment, I thought I had finally succeeded in shutting him up. I took in a long, deep breath and tried to release some tension as I exhaled. And then I heard the same deep voice again:

"Please don't do this to me. You have no idea how hard this is for me." He hung his head on his chest and shook it slightly. And then he looked to his right and started to fumble for the door handle. Unable to find it, he began to push on the door.

"*Nooo!*" I screamed, and my heart jumped into my throat. I reached over and grabbed his hand that was on his side of the door, jerking the car left and right.

All hell broke loose.

"*I have no idea?* What idea do you have? Do you know how tired I am? Do you know how hard this day has been for me? How hard it is to carry on like this? Do you have any idea how hard I try to help you and help us? Do you know that all this trouble is for your sake? You are not helping! Where do you want to go? *Tell me! Anywhere you want to go, I will go!* I will do whatever you know what to do. But I cannot go if you don't know where! You've got to give me a way to do it. *If you want to go, go!*"

Words shot out of my mouth like bullets fired from an assault rifle by a madwoman. "Do you know how difficult this has been for me? Do you know how hard it is to deal with your confusion, with my demanding career, and with a gloomy future? Do you know that I don't even dare to feel scared, tired, depressed, or lonely, because then I wouldn't be able to carry on?

"I am so tired. I am so, so tired! But I can't even think of myself. Who is going to help me? You? How can you help me when you need to be helped with everything? I get no help from you, only continued trouble. I am human, too. I have my limits, and I can be broken. You are crushing me! You are killing me! I have no one to lean on. I am all alone. Do you know how exhausted I am? If you want to go, go! I can't take it anymore!"

The sadness and frustration that had been densely packed inside me for the past two years rushed out like the volatile waters of the Yellow River reaching a breached dike, with a force within it that was stronger than itself. I could no longer steady the steering wheel or focus on the road, so I turned the car into the Firewheel Town Center mall parking lot. I stopped the engine, rolled down the window, and burst into gut-wrenching wailing. I bawled at the top of my voice, like a wounded animal, rocking back and forth over the wheel.

"What can I do? It is so hard. What can I do?"

"I cannot do it anymore. Baby, do you understand me? I cannot do it anymore."

"What am I going to do?"

My questions echoed over the cold, unsympathetic parking lot and disappeared into the silent and unfathomable obscurity beyond. The vast parking lot was utterly deserted, engulfed by darkness except for our headlights, minuscule and so fragile, so lonely, and so insignificant.

I don't know how much time passed. Eventually, my violent lamentations abated. I leaned on the steering wheel, my head resting on my arms, still sobbing. As if a bucket full of dirty water had been emptied, the weight pressing on me was lightened, and my sense and sensibility gradually returned. I became aware of Clyde, sitting in the passenger seat, lost.

"Hon, are you all right?" the clueless one asked, in a very concerned voice.

Of course not! I sat up, wiping away my tears with the back of my hand, unable to stop the convulsions.

"What is wrong, Hon?"

Everything.

Hearing no response from me, Clyde put his left hand on my back, patting me gently as if I were a little girl.

"Hon, you know I love you. If there is anything wrong, talk to me."

His touch and his words were so tender and familiar. They belonged to the Clyde I had fallen in love with fifteen years ago. My heart swelled. Another surge of tears flooded my eyes.

Where did you go, Clyde? I need you.

Without a word, no longer angry but with profound sadness and a great deal of self-reproach, I started the car and continued on to the lake house. I kept Clyde's hand on my back to feel anchored. Miraculously, the infuriating declaration "I want to go home" didn't recur for the remaining ten minutes of our drive.

We got to the lake house after one o'clock in the morning. I turned up the heat and made hot chamomile tea for us. After that, I filled the Jacuzzi tub and we soaked in the hot, bubbling water. Like a little child, Clyde bathed himself ineptly, wiping here and there with a washcloth, missing many parts of his pale, skinny body. I dried him, helped him to bed, and tucked him in. Finally, I lay my aching body next to his. Laying my head on his shoulder and wrapping one of my arms around his chest, I whispered into his ear, "Baby, I am sorry."

Not remembering can sometimes be a great blessing. With that thought, I turned over, closed my eyes, and, as the famous words of Scarlett O'Hara in *Gone with the Wind* came to my mind, I mumbled:

"After all, tomorrow is another day."

Such outbursts, however ugly and painful, were like storms, dissipating as fast as they began. We human beings have an incredible ability to adapt to our surroundings in order to survive. After the initial years, I began to adjust to a life filled with Clyde's forgetfulness, confusion, repetitions, anxiety, agitation, sundowning, and occasional hallucinations. I developed more realistic expectations and coping strategies; I also learned the importance of acknowledging and accepting my own limitations.

While I gradually grew out of my temper tantrums, a more persistent dark force began to challenge the better angels of my nature: depression. Everyone feels low sometimes, but well spouses are especially susceptible to prolonged and persistent episodes of depression. *Et donner un sens à sa vie*—life needs meaning. For most people, love gives life clear meaning, and a beloved life partner is irreplaceable when it comes to the human desire for someone to share our innermost thoughts with. By 2008, Clyde had been living with Alzheimer's for six years, and I had been mourning the loss of my life partner for all that time. His ability to communicate in any meaningful way was long gone, and a recent stroke had rendered him mostly immobile. Completely dependent, he was now receiving hospice care. Although not to be feared, the approaching death of someone so dear to me felt very close; yet it was so unknown to me it also seemed quite remote. Waiting and wondering locked my life into a perpetual limbo, the future shrouded in a thick, dark fog, unfathomable, surreal.

Is death indeed upon us? How soon?
How much pain will I feel?
What's next in my life?

In his novel *Lincoln in the Bardo*, George Saunders describes the kind of depression I felt: "His mind was freshly inclined toward *sorrow*; toward the fact that the world was full of sorrow; that everyone labored under some burden of sorrow; that all were suffering; that whatever way one took in this world, one must try to remember that all were suffering (none content; all wronged, neglected, overlooked, misunderstood). . . ."[60] My work at SMU, which had always filled me with great pride and satisfaction, was suffering. I felt alienated from my friends. It was hard for my son or anyone else close to me to understand my struggles. Money was pouring out of the bank. Every day there were outsiders (caregivers, medical staff) in my home, and their continual presence sucked the air out of me.

I went to see the doctor about my depressive symptoms: sadness, crying, not wanting to get up in the morning, not knowing what to look forward to each day, seeing no hope for happiness in my future.

"Do you feel trapped in this situation?" he asked me. Young, competent, and genuinely caring, he inspired trust, and I liked him. He understood my circumstances, since he had been Clyde's physician as well until Clyde went to Monticello, where it was more convenient for him to see Monticello's in-house doctors.

"Do I feel trapped?" I thought for a while, searching inside. I had never asked myself that question. "No. I don't feel trapped. I know I have choices." Clyde had made sure that he wouldn't deprive me of the freedom to live the way I wanted. I knew that my power of attorney gave me the freedom to divorce him and move on, if I wished. "But I just don't seem to know what to hope for. I am unable to feel happy the way I used to."

Medication and therapy alleviated my symptoms somewhat. But it was the knowledge that I did have choices that provided me an anchor. There was no perfect choice, and we often don't know for sure what the best option might be in any given situation. Yet we must choose what makes the most sense at each turn and go on from there.

Being perceptive about having choices helped me to move forward.

I recognized that there was a symbiotic relationship between pain and happiness: deep in the heart of every human being, there is a kind of pain and also a window to happiness. Without pain, there is no path to happiness; without happiness, one cannot learn the bitter taste of pain.

If pain and hurt are unavoidable, let me grow stronger in coping with these feelings. And let me learn to listen to the better angels of my nature.

And I remembered the following passage, though I forget where it came from: "People may not always act evolved, enlightened, civilized, compassionate; it may not come easily, it may not come at all, and we may have to go deeper beyond what comes easily and naturally at the moment. For some, it will not come at all, but for most of us, it always does if we let it."

"When a man has lost all happiness, he is not alive. Call him a breathing corpse," Sophocles of Kolōnos sermonized.

"All things are only transitory," Johann Wolfgang von Goethe consoled.

". . . when again touched, as surely they will be, by the better angels of our nature," Abraham Lincoln encouraged.

Life went on through a season that recalled the winter weather of Shanghai as I had known it in my childhood: cloudy, cold, dark and damp, often windy and rainy, with occasional blue skies and sunshine. I wondered if there really was a God who was punishing me for having had an unfair amount of happiness in my life with Clyde before his illness and who was now evening the score by taking happiness away from me.

"You need a dog. You need someone to come home to, someone who will be waiting for you and happy to see you," said Charlie. They had been nudging me for a while to get a dog. They themselves had three four-legged furry babies, all spoiled rotten.

"I love going home knowing my Emily is there to give me kisses and hugs." Ronnie was referring to their little female shih tzu. She weighed just nine pounds but was already severely obese. She only took food from Ronnie's palm.

"If you had a dog, it would give you kisses too," Charlie said, smiling contentedly as if Clark, a male dog they had rescued, were licking his face.

"My Lily knows that she is my first love. Chuck is my second." Ronnie never missed an opportunity to be obnoxious. "She sleeps with me every night."

"Whaateeever." Charlie rolled his eyes and stretched those vowels.

I have always been an animal lover. I adore anything and everything alive and hairy, furry, feathery, or fuzzy, with legs or wings. When I was growing up in Shanghai, no family was allowed to have pets. But that did not prevent me from bringing home a pretty baby rat one day when I was in the fourth grade. Barely a week old with a white coat and red eyes, she was sneaked out by someone from a research lab. It was the cutest little life I had ever held in my hands. I fed her a little milk I had skimmed from Dad's rations and kept her in a shoebox, in the top of which I had carefully punched holes to let air in. I lined the inside with soft cotton. It was the best home I could have made for her, and I made sure she was comfortable. I begged and nagged my parents to let me keep her. All night long, I thought of my little friend keeping warm in her box in the kitchen, and I worried over whether Mom and Dad would make me get rid of her. When morning finally came, I rushed into the kitchen to see her, but the little pretty had chewed a hole in the shoebox and run away. Within weeks, our home was infested with spotted gray-and-white rats. I can still picture Dad in the hallway swinging a long-handled broom, angrily chasing the spotted rats as they scurried, terrified, in all directions. My parents and siblings have never failed to remind me of the disastrous consequences of my foolish compassion for the ungrateful little furry pretty.

Now I was free to have any pet I chose, but how could I be sure that I would be able to care for a dog on top of caring for my husband; for Charlie, who had cancer; for Ronnie and my son, Stuey, who both had yet to grow up; for myself, and taking care of my job?

"Let's just go and look," Charlie and Ronnie tempted me.

Together we visited animal shelters near and far all over Dallas. I fell in love with many dogs and made commitments to none, until the fateful encounter that ended my search. A litter of puppies was born to Charlie's brother's family dog. We went "just to look at them," with the result that I came home with not one but two most loving and beautiful puppies.

I named them Meemee, the Chinese word for "honey," and Huanhuan, meaning "happy." They were barely six weeks old, their tiny eyes the size of little peas and not yet fully open, their coats still fuzzy and not yet furry, and each with a different pattern of black and white.

"Salt and pepper?" Looking at them, people smiled.

"Yin and yang," I responded, smiling back, referring to the Chinese symbol for balance and harmony.

Meemee and Huanhuan gave my life renewed meaning and happiness with one simple element: unconditional love. With their angel-like gazes and innocent expressions, waggling tails, passionate kisses, and delightful cuddles, they made it easy for my better angels to stay.

At last I was able to understand completely why Emily Dickinson said, "Dogs are better than human beings because they know but do not tell." My furry pretties never told me that, despite their mama's admonition against human food, Uncle Charlie and Uncle Ronnie frequently slipped them forbidden treats.

The author with her canine babies, Lake Ray Hubbard, Rowlett, Texas.

ARLINGTON HOTEL,
Hot Springs, Ark.

S. H. STITT & CO.,
Proprietors.

This elegant establishment, recently constructed, with ample accommodations for **200 guests,** offers unusual attractions and inducements to the public. It is the **only hotel** at the Hot Springs that can claim pre-eminence as a **first-class** house of entertainment, being the **best regulated** and **best sustained** in the South.

THE ARLINGTON

Is supplied with all the comforts, conveniences and luxuries of modern times, and boasts the latest improvements in the art of hostelry.

A vintage poster of Arlington Hotel.

Eighteen

RETURN TO HOT SPRINGS

A year ago, on this day, in this doorway,	去年今日此門中，
Your face and the peach blooms echoed each other's rosy glow.	人面桃花香映紅。
Where you have gone, I do not know;	人面不知何處去，
The peach blooms still smile in the spring breeze.	桃花依舊笑春風。

—CUI HU (崔护),
Lines on South Village, Near the Capital (題都城南庄), Tang Dynasty, ca. 790[61]

FALL 2009. THE SEMESTER HAD JUST STARTED. Absorbed in caregiving all through the hectic summer, like a drowning person floundering desperately for air, I longed for an opportunity to get away from the caregiving before facing a more hectic fall semester. After the first week of class came Labor Day, a long weekend. I was ready to go somewhere, anywhere, for a little R & R. It would have to be a short trip: Clyde could have another stroke, and the condition of Charlie, who was battling cancer, was not yet stable. I didn't want to go anywhere without Meemee and Huanhuan, my two baby canines who were my companions and therapy.

But where to?

Chicago? Spending time with my brother and his family, who lived there, had always been pleasant. I would be with the people who loved me and in the vibrant city where I started my American journey twenty-three years earlier. Meemee and Huanhuan had had fun harassing Coco the Cat last time, and there was an amazing incident that my sister-in-law still tells at the family get-together. In one of our visits shortly after Clyde's diagnosis, I had warned them that during the night Clyde might get confused about which room was ours. Sure enough one night my sister-in-law was gently pushed awake in the dark by a man, naked. It frightened her but she quickly realized that it was Clyde fumbling to get back to bed after using the bathroom. She took him back to me as I slept like a log in the next room. No one had afforded me more unconditional acceptance than my brother's family. But it turned out to be unfeasible this time. Airlines have strict policies for dogs to ride in the cabin. I would be able to take one of the dogs, not both. It was quite a traumatic experience for them to be put into the luggage compartment last time we went to Chicago, and the temperature in Dallas was too high for them to ride in the luggage compartment anyway. Scanning my database of the US geography within a three-hundred-mile radius of Dallas yielded one promising destination: Hot Springs, Arkansas, 292 miles away. *Perfect!*

A plaque in front of the Arlington Hotel.

Once claiming the title of "The American Spa," Hot Springs was just four and a half hours from Dallas by car. It had lots of pet-friendly hotels. In addition, the trip there made it possible for me to fulfill an unfulfilled dream.

Four years before, in the spring of 2005, Clyde had already lived with the diagnosis of Alzheimer's disease for over two years. Feeling that time was running short, I launched an excursion to trace Clyde's roots before it was too late. We took a sentimental journey eastward from Dallas to Arkansas, where he—Clyde Joye Wingfield—started his worldly existence. The trip first brought us to Curtis, Arkansas, a "populated place" on the map that did not qualify as a town in Clyde's time, and still does not qualify as a town today. Along the way, we paid respect to his parents at their gravesides, where we placed flowers, and drove by his high school and junior college in Arkadelphia. Our final stop was Hot Springs, Arkansas.

That trip to Hot Springs left a lingering regret: I didn't get to enjoy The American Spa. Clyde was not too keen on the spa experience. For him, it was "much ado about nothing."

"If I want a hot bath, I would take a hot bath," he insisted.

Those were the days when if I took my eyes away from him for ten seconds, he could have walked out of the room to look for his Hon and gotten lost, even if I was in the same hotel room and told him a hundred times, "Do not go out without me. I am in the bathroom." There was no way I could leave him in the hotel room and go for a spa treatment. My desire for a "hot bath" never materialized.

During that stay in the Arlington Hotel, every evening as we took a walk inside the hotel, we would pass through the Crystal Ballroom, Venetian Room, Magnolia Room, Writing Room, and Music Room and then by the spa entrance. I would peep into it, wondering, envyingly, how nice it would feel to have that "hot bath" and get some pampering. Because I had never tried a spa, it remained mysterious to me.

So I drank an extra amount of the steaming hot mineral water flowing endlessly from the hotel lobby fountain to make up for my loss. As we drove away from Hot Springs, I said to Clyde jokingly, "I am sure I am the only woman who came to Hot Springs and left without a hot bath!"

"I promise you I will take you back next time and you will have your hot bath," he said.

This time, my canines and I arrived at Hot Springs just before dusk. As we turned on Central Avenue, which cuts through downtown, the Arlington Hotel's familiar and formative figure stood in front of us. My heart ached.

Clyde, we are here again.

. . . on this day, in this doorway, where have you gone? I do not know.

The legendary Arlington Hotel looked even older than last time. The big fountain in the lobby was still dispensing steaming hot mineral water endlessly. The spa still offered a thermal bath, or "hot bath," as Clyde referred to it, and all other head-to-toe pampering. Upon check-in, I immediately made a reservation for a thermal bath and some head-to-toe pampering. The earliest availability would be the next day. So wait till tomorrow I must.

If I want a hot bath, I would take a hot bath. Clyde's voice was ringing in my head.

Within five minutes, I unpacked, changed into my walking shoes, collected my two little canine children, and went out on the streets in search of a dinner for three. We walked up and down Central Avenue and finally spotted a small restaurant that seemed promising. I pushed the door open, asking tentatively, "Can we eat here?" I added, "Me and my babies?"

The waitress's eyes lingered on my face and then moved down to the two little furry faces. Six expectant eyes were all looking back at her.

"I peeked." I pressed gently. "You are not too busy tonight. You can tell that these babies will not disturb other patrons."

She was not sure.

Encouraged by her silence (hey, until I was rejected, it was promising!), I added more smile, which I believed was hard to resist. "Please." My babies wiggled their tails in sync to echo my plea.

That obviously worked. "We normally do not allow dogs in our restaurant," the waitress said. "Go outside of the building and come around to the patio through the parking lot."

We were elated with our success. The babies and I high-fived each other and raced up the hill, up the stairs, through the rooftop parking lot, down some narrow and slippery steps and up, and there we were, on a small wooden patio nestled in the cliffs on three sides, with one side connecting to the restaurant's formal dining room facing the street. The patio was barely illuminated by strands of white Christmas lights, which were wrapped around the trunks of the fan palm trees standing in giant planters, and flickering candles on the tables. The air was warm and moist. The atmosphere felt tropical and wistful. Among the seven or eight tables, only two were occupied.

Clyde, I wish you were here. You would have liked it.

"What sounds good to you tonight, my darling?" He would never fail to give me instruction on anything and everything. "Order anything you want."

After Alzheimer's disease robbed him of his ability to read and comprehend written words, he would say, "Hon, why don't you order for me? You know what I like."

And for all my love for him, I would order what I liked for him, and I would order what I liked for me.

And he would be happy, and I would be happy.

It was a Friday evening. I went downstairs to the lobby. The band was already playing, and the lobby was already filled with people. I ordered a piña colada at the bar. There wasn't a single spot available in the area where the band was playing. The bar scene had never been my scene. Looking up, I saw that the mezzanine overlooking the lobby was completely empty.

Marvelous!

Looking around from the mezzanine, one couldn't help but reminisce on the hotel's past. The Arlington Hotel first opened in 1875. After the 1893 rebuild, author Charles Cutter referred to it as "the most elegant and complete hotel in America" in his 1892 *Cutter's Guide to the Hot Springs of Arkansas*. According to the hotel website, the Arlington's luxurious accommodations, rooms with piped-in thermal mineral waters, and the in-hotel bathhouse have attracted famous and infamous guests, such as presidents Franklin Roosevelt, Harry Truman, George H. W. Bush, and Bill Clinton; celebrities such as Tony Bennett, Barbra Streisand, and Yoko Ono; and baseball players such as Babe Ruth. Al Capone's favorite room

The hotel lobby. The stage where the band plays is seen at the back. Photo from TripAdvisor.

was 443, and he occupied an entire floor to house his staff and bodyguards while staying there. Across from his window he could see the Southern Club, a gambling house famous for gangsters in the 1930s, now the Wax Museum.

From the mezzanine, with the piña colada in my hand, I had a clear view of the entire band and the dance floor. The band seemed to be the same one as when we were there last time. Three guys were playing: a piano, a trumpet, and percussion. Two guys were senior in age, or "mature," as Clyde would call it. One of them doubled as a vocalist. Unlike the music on the street that night (a blues festival was going on that weekend), the music being played here was unhurried, and the songs being sung here were unhurried.

Several couples were dancing; some were young, most old, and all appeared to be happy. I studied the older couples. Their dancing appeared to be more methodical, more dignified and graceful. Judging from how harmonious their body movements were, I tried to guess whether each couple had been together for a long time and whether they still had flames for each other or whether that once-fierce fire of passion that would have engulfed everything had burnt out, leaving simmering flickers, warm and safe.

Enjoy, people, enjoy life, enjoy each other, for tomorrow may not be the same.

Last time we were there, we sat on the big plush couch in the center of the lobby. I was sipping a piña colada, and Clyde was nursing a glass of cabernet sauvignon. We danced mostly to slow and moderate tunes. It didn't matter to us how well we danced. All that mattered was that we were together, and we enjoyed every moment of being with each other. Dance enabled a level of physical harmony that seemed to complete our psychological and intellectual synchronization; even the differences and disagreements became complementary in our coexistence—in making us whole. For that brief moment on the Arlington dance floor, Clyde was so relaxed. We left the shadow of illness someplace else, no anxiety, no worries, no need to deal with the loss of faculties, and no ugly face of Alzheimer's.

After two or three rounds of dances, we would return to our seats to take a break. Then when the right music came up again, Clyde would grow enthusiastic. "Hon, would you like to dance this one with me?" With both his arms extending, he asked with that Southern boy politeness.

Other times, he'd be tired. "Let's go sit down."

"Over the hill?" I would tease him, hoping he would take my bait, and predictably he would.

"No. I am not tired. Do you really want to dance this one?"

"Yes." I figured a little push of his physical limitation would do him good, and we would dance some more.

Then the music would change to a fast and crazier rhythm. The happy feeling was contagious, and more couples would swirl onto the dance floor. Clyde would say, "Let's wait it out." He did not like to dance to fast beats, nor did I.

"*You* are tired," he would tell me. "Let's go sit down." The Wingfield Confidence would not let him admit that it was *he* who was tired.

At one point, a slow and familiar tune began playing again. It was "Sentimental Journey," recorded in 1945 by Les Brown's orchestra with Doris Day as the vocalist. Most couples returned to their seats to take a break from dancing to the crazier rhythm. Clyde started to hum along. He had a vast repository of songs and music. He sang along with every tune in his baritone voice, and he had a song for every occasion.

"Do you know this one?" he asked at the next tune.

Of course, I did not know what the song was.

"I think it is from the musical *West Side Story*." He started humming Maria's "I Feel Pretty."

Of course, I had not heard of *West Side Story*.

Clyde could not hide his satisfaction. He had just made another contribution to my Americanization.

Then we were dancing to the tune of Sinatra's "New York, New York."

"If I can make it there, I'll make it anywhere. . . ." Clyde's voice still rang in my mind.

You have absolutely made it, Clyde!

The next day, I finally had my long-anticipated thermal bath and spa treatment. After two hours of soaking, scrubbing, rubbing, kneading, pressing, stretching, and other oh-so-good-for-you stuff, I felt rejuvenated. When I returned to my hotel room, there was Clyde, sitting on the maroon wingback chair by the window with a smile on his face.

How was the hot bath, Hon?

Arlington Hotel, Hot Springs National Park, Arkansas, 2009.

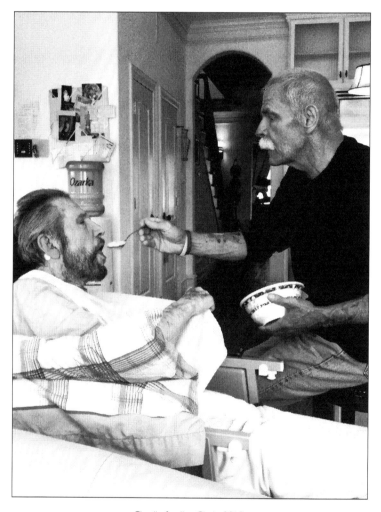

Charlie feeding Clyde, 2010.

Nineteen

HON, ARE YOU THERE?

A shadow flits before me,
Not thou, but like to thee:
Ah Christ, that it were possible
For one short hour to see
The souls we loved, that they might tell us
What and where they be.

—LORD ALFRED TENNYSON, Maud: A Monodrama (part II)

L ATE AUTUMN. THE DAYS WERE GETTING SHORTER. Before dinnertime, the room was already in shadow. The man sat in the big blue chair in the family room, his body frail and emaciated, making the chair appear almost empty. His fine gray hair rested delicately on his head. His face was pallid, and in the dusty light his eyes had taken on an ineffable color. Gray? Green? Blue? Or was it light brown? Gazing blankly in front of him as if he saw something in the air that was visible only to him, he stretched out his right arm, fingers unsteady, trying to touch the apparition in the void.

"Are you there, Lan Jiang?" He struggled to lean forward a little, extending his bent arm further. His voice sounded weary. "Hon, are you there?"

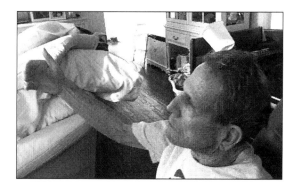

"Hon, are you there?"

The scene called to mind Charlotte Brontë's *Jane Eyre*. Jane, having fled Thornfield Hall on her wedding night after discovering that she cannot marry Mr. Rochester, begins a new life far from him. Then one day, mysteriously, she hears his voice repeating her name, letting her know that he is in distress. She returns to Thornfield and learns that his former mentally ill wife has burnt the grand manor to ruins, losing her life in the process. Jane locates Mr. Rochester in Ferndean, a desolate country house of "considerable antiquity, moderate size, and no architectural pretensions, deep buried in a wood." As Jane enters the dimly lit room, Mr. Rochester, sitting in his chair, alone, asks upon hearing her familiar voice, "Is it Jane?" He reaches out for her: "Jane Eyre! Jane Eyre!" The fire has left him blind and disfigured with only one hand.[62]

But this autumn afternoon scene was not in a novel from Victorian England. It was from my life in the fall of 2009, in the sprawling city of Dallas.

"Clyde, Baby, I am here. I am right here with you. Do you see me now?" I had been washing vegetables in the kitchen. Putting the greens in the sink, I dried my hands with a kitchen towel and walked over to Clyde—I was fewer than ten steps away from him. Like Jane Eyre, I "arrested his wandering hand, and prisoned it in both mine."

Slowly, Clyde turned his eyes toward me and focused his gaze on my face. He freed his hand and moved it up tentatively to feel my face, as if he could tell by touching it that the woman in front of him was really Lan Jiang, his Hon.

A trace of a smile rippled over his face. "Oh, here you are."

In August, a few weeks earlier, I had brought Clyde home to live with me again in the big-and-beautiful house. When Clyde went to Monticello in October 2007, I had mourned, grieved, sobbed, self-doubted, and struggled with guilt and depression. I had thought that Clyde would never again return to this house that we had built together and shared with each other. I had accepted as my fate that Clyde's living away from the home we shared was eternal. How wrong I was!

Once again, Clyde's presence filled our home. His adjustable hospital bed, courtesy of Medicare, stood flush against the west wall in the family room, next to the open kitchen and the powder room. His medications occupied a big shoebox sitting prominently atop the granite counter with its pattern resembling a Chinese brush painting. His laundry, which seemed endless, was spread out on the couch, emitting the scents of Tide and Clorox. The aroma of his food—chicken and dumplings, meatloaf, or soup of some sort—permeated the entire house, including every hairline crack of the walls. The sounds of his coughing and mumbling echoed in every corner, as did the commotion of the ever-present caregivers as they came and went, greeting and chatting with each other and exchanging care notes. There was a constant flurry as they adjusted Clyde's position to relieve pressure points on his bottom, hips, and legs; lifted him to use the toilet; and cleaned up his frequent messy accidents. That sometimes included feces being trodden by caregivers who were in such a hurry or so inexperienced, absentminded, or preoccupied with their own problems that they didn't notice they had brought the nasty stuff all over the house as if a landmine had exploded.

Clyde's being back home was just one example of expecting the unexpected. In the movie *Forrest Gump*, Forrest, played by Tom Hanks, often quotes his mama: "My mom always said life was like a box of chocolates. You never know what you're gonna get."

Yes, a cliché often becomes a cliché because it is true.

—⚘—

Moving Clyde back home was possible because, after his stroke in June 2008, he stopped pacing through the house, pushing things, and breaking things. He no longer posed a danger to himself or others. But moving him home had become necessary because of Charlie's cancer treatment. Charlie underwent radiation and chemo with admirable endurance, and with the help of his ever-devoted partner, Ronnie. As expected, their availability to help Clyde and me became limited and unpredictable. It was now much easier and more economical than it had been before to care for Clyde at home, so I posted a caregiver needed notice in the local Chinese paper and hired a Chinese woman to split the time with Charlie and Ronnie. Clyde no longer spoke, so the language barrier was not a concern anymore. Chinese caregivers usually had values similar to mine on many matters of household management—for example, they were generally thrifty and relentlessly clean, and they didn't even bother to turn on the TV because of their limited English. Also, I was glad that I could offer them something that I might not be able to offer Americans—helping them improve their English and learn more about American customs. They looked up to me as someone who understood not only Chinese but also English, who had assimilated into, instead of alienated herself from, the mainstream culture so could help them learn to navigate this country. They often appreciated being able to communicate with me in Chinese and felt comfortable working for me.

Last but not least, predictably and persistently, they always removed their shoes when coming inside the house.

In her memoir *Dirty Details*, Marion Deutsche Cohen, who spent many years as a well spouse during her husband's battle with multiple sclerosis, uses three simple yet incisive words to describe "the days and nights of a well spouse": *nights, lifting, and toilet.*[63] I now found that my own life centered on those three things. Our caregivers—Charlie, Ronnie, and others—helped with most of the lifting and toileting, while nights were strictly my territory. Nothing about the tasks connected with those three categories was easy. At times, being the well spouse was so horrendously difficult that I wondered about the very meaning of the spousal relationship and even life itself, as I struggled to sustain a sense of the fundamental purpose of living. Finding happiness, or even peace of mind, sometimes seemed almost impossible.

In her book, Cohen wonders at one point whether it would be possible, after being the well spouse for so long, to resume her former relationship with her ill spouse even if he were to miraculously recover: "The role you played as a caretaker, a servant, a nurse, a mother-like figure is so completely apart from a lover." As the spousal relationship changes, it is entirely plausible that the feelings behind it would change, too. The love that once welded two lives together may lose much of its power in the face of unanticipated challenges, leaving the well spouse and the ill spouse revolving out of their original orbit onto separate paths. It does not surprise me that some well spouses want to run away from caregiving; some actually do.

Each well spouse may have his or her own set of circumstances. Cohen's situation is vastly different from mine: they were young with children. Being young parents, they had more financial constraints. Although her husband was much more impaired physically than mentally, she was a well spouse for a staggering twenty-four years, with her husband spending the last nine years in a nursing home. Debilitating illnesses are terrible to deal with at any age, but Marion Cohen and her husband were deprived of what should have been the prime years of their careers and family life. Her account, though angry and bitter, is honest.

Other than the occasional fast-come, fast-gone outbursts in my early years as a well spouse, I felt no lasting anger or bitterness as a well spouse, but I did encounter frustration and depression. On particularly awful days, when depressive thoughts about the right to pursue happiness and about my relationship with my husband entered my mind, I always came back to the fundamental question: Do I have a choice? Ultimately, I chose to stay directly involved in his care. My choice had to do with our specific but not unique situation. We had invested love, consideration, and mutual respect in our relationship before Clyde became ill, which gave me a great deal of emotional capital. We had built a solid financial foundation during our long, challenging, and rewarding careers, so I was afforded choices such as caring for Clyde in an assisted-living facility and with hired caregivers. I was younger than he and still had plenty of physical strength. Our family and friends stood by me and provided me emotional support, and I nurtured good relationships with hired caregivers, which allowed me some degree of freedom.

I am keenly aware that many well spouses and other family caregivers are less fortunate than I was, and there is no one-size-fits-all model for spousal caregiving, but finding the right balance is the key to whether the well spouse will find a way to carry on or choose the path to move on with his or her own life.

One morning, from my bedroom upstairs, I could hear Charlie and Ronnie in the family room getting Clyde up. As I came downstairs, I heard Charlie talking to Clyde.

"Mr. Wingfield, do you have any meetings to attend today?" Charlie still talked to him as if he could understand.

"Da da da," Clyde mumbled. That was all that was left in the vocabulary of my once-eloquent husband. "Da da da baba." He was waving something at Charlie, almost triumphantly.

"What is that in Clyde's hand?" I asked Charlie. And then I saw it: the soiled disposable underwear Clyde had managed to pull out from underneath himself.

"Clyde wanted to let me know that he did it." Charlie took the diaper from Clyde's hand. It looked heavy, saturated with the aqueous solution filled with organic and inorganic compounds—urea, chloride, sodium, potassium, and all sorts of other God-knows-what good stuff. It had a distinctively pungent smell.

"It was just number one," Charlie added. He had read my mind.

"No number two? You have checked, right?" Having had to deal with frequent feces attacks since Clyde's return home, I was naturally nervous.

"Yes, ma'am," Charlie assured me.

Although Clyde's left arm could hardly move after the stroke, his right arm remained strong and active. He grabbed everything within his reach—newspapers, towels, napkins—and tried to bite whatever he got hold of. Sometimes I put the puppies on his lap. He once picked up Huanhuan and attempted to bite him. Another time, he held my hand to his mouth. I thought he was going to give it an affectionate kiss, but instead he started to bite my fingers. He even bit his own fingers and screamed in pain. He was very fond of pinching the butts of people who were standing by him. I believe he would have bitten them if he could have managed to get them close to his mouth. At night, we wrapped his hands in mittens to stop him from biting his fingers, pulling off his disposable underwear, or scratching his own face.

Other than occasionally frowning or raising his eyebrows, Clyde did not express much in the way of anything. He was often withdrawn and seemed despondent. The doctor thought that Clyde could die anytime, so he remained in hospice care but didn't seem to be going anywhere in a hurry. Life for him became merely a basic existence.

Clyde's bodily functions were a daily subject of discussion among us, especially his bowel movements. There was either too much of it, so that we had to spend a lot of time cleaning up the mess, or not enough, forcing us to induce a movement.

One day, Charlie was telling the hospice nurse about Clyde's constipation. "He hasn't moved since the day before yesterday. I am afraid to give him a laxative because he had diarrhea for several days last week after the last one I gave him."

While Charlie was talking, Clyde was sitting in his big blue chair as usual, indifferent, as if the conversation had nothing to do with him.

"Let's use an enema. I have one here," the nurse said. "Let's get him on his belly so we can put it in more easily."

At that, Clyde's deep voice uttered loudly, clearly, and firmly, "Hell, you will not!"

Everyone stood stunned, and then everyone laughed. But they went ahead with the enema in spite of his opposition.

By the end of 2009, the radiation and chemo had still had little effect on Charlie's cancer. The only thing left to try was a stem cell transplant. Without it, the doctor was quite certain that Charlie would have only about four months to live. With the transplant, there was hope for a longer life. But there was a caveat: in those days, only one in four recipients was likely to survive the stem cell transplant.

Charlie and Ronnie came for their shift and told me about their grim task of picking the lesser of two evils. I revealed to them that I was a hawk disguised as a dove: I believed in the ancient wisdom "no pain, no gain" and would choose to butt heads with cancer. I would rather face the unknown, take the stem cell transplant, and hope for the best than to accept a four-month life with a death sentence. With Clyde in his big blue chair next to them as if he were sitting in as an *ex officio* member of the committee, the two of them sat on the couch in the family room, holding hands, talking, weeping, and embracing each other. They decided to take the 25 percent chance that Charlie would survive the transplant. When Charlie became ill in 2007, they hired an attorney and set up all their end-of-life designations, granting each other power of attorney and appointing each other guardian and agent for the disposition of the remains. They were certain that family members who didn't approve of their homosexual relationship would try to take away their right to take care of each other. They knew that they did not have the same legal rights as married couples did to protect their desire to handle each other's affairs when one of them had been incapacitated or worse, deceased, because same-sex marriage was illegal in Texas. Now that their paramount fear was gone, they were prepared for the worst while hoping for the best.

On Christmas Eve 2009, Charlie had the stem cell transplant. During that process, the intensive chemotherapy attacked his blood cells, both cancerous and not, and destroyed his body's ability to generate new blood cells. The stem cells that had been previously harvested from his body were then returned to his veins; it was as though he had been reborn. On the following day, Christmas, one of the nurses brought a cake to Charlie's room with one lit candle. His doctors and other care staff came in, too. Everyone sang, "Happy birthday to Charlie, and many more."

But how many more?

Clyde had threatened to die for a year and a half. He was still receiving hospice care, but he was still with us. Charlie was young, only fifty-three. He had to win this battle. It would take ten days before we knew whether the stem cells would be able to make new, healthy blood cells to sustain his life. Counting each passing day as a triumph, we waited, held our breath, and hid our fear.

With both Clyde's and Charlie's lives hanging by a thread, 2010 arrived without much fanfare. Then day ten came. Charlie had crossed the first, most crucial threshold!

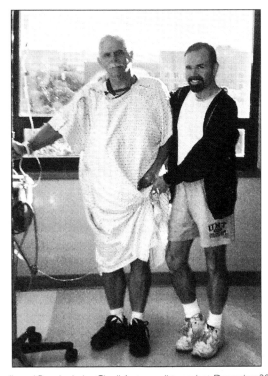

Charlie and Ronnie during Charlie's stem cell transplant, December 2008.

August 21, 2010. A long day was over. The caregivers were gone. All was quiet. Lying in bed, I felt relieved and relaxed. Downstairs, Clyde was tucked in securely. Other than changing his diaper during the night, I shouldn't have to deal with any more struggles until the next morning. I picked up the novel that I was halfway through, Lisa Genova's *Still Alice*, trying to step out of the life of a well spouse and get into a world where pain, confusion, crises, and anxiety belonged to fictional characters.

But the story brought me right back to where I was. The novel is about an intelligent, energetic professor's gradual descent into darkness due to early-onset Alzheimer's disease. At one point, the afflicted professor, Alice, talks with her daughter:

> "You're so beautiful," said Alice. "I'm so afraid of looking at you and not knowing who you are."
>
> "I think that even if you don't know who I am someday, you'll still know that I love you."
>
> "What if I see you, and I don't know that you're my daughter, and I don't know that you love me?"
>
> "Then, I'll tell you that I do, and you'll believe me."[64]

This dialogue reminded me of the early stages of Clyde's Alzheimer's disease following his diagnosis. One day I found him down, depressed and full of sadness, which was unusual for him. His mood didn't seem to differ much regardless of the happenings around him. At Baruch College, his colleagues characterized their president, jokingly and endearingly, as being "even-tempered, always mean." That was before he was ill.

I asked him what was wrong.

"I am scared." His head hung down over his chest like a flag at half-mast whipped wet by the rain, and his eyes were teary, also rare for my "guy's guy" fear-no-evil husband. "I don't know what's happening to me. I don't know where I am."

My heart ached. I held his head against my chest as if comforting a frightened baby, and then cradled his face in both of my hands so I could look deep into his eyes. I said to him, slowly and deliberately, trying to pound every word firmly into his head:

"Listen to me, Baby. Wherever you are, wherever you go, when everything around you disappears, always remember that I love you. Always know that I will take care of you. Put these words deep inside your consciousness. Never let them go. Even when nothing is left in your world, my love will still be with you."

All was gone. Now that even the last name in his memory, Lan Jiang, my name, had faded away, he had no one left. He was alone in a vast ocean with no shores.

Baby, I hope that somewhere in your being, my love still makes you feel safe.

I set the book down by my pillow and looked at the right-hand side of the bed, where Clyde had always slept. I rolled over to his side, wondering if I could still detect the indentation left by his body or any other trace of his presence. Longing swept over me, intense and strong. My heart achingly yearned to be with my Clyde. Distant memories flared up like rekindled fire: the warmth of his body, the scent of his flesh, the sound of his breath, the feeling of his touch, and the sensation of my nose rubbing his hair, the fur.

"You white people are definitely less evolved creatures," I teased him while sniffing his fur, "who came down from the trees not very long ago."

I told him that it was a scientific fact that as human beings evolve, they lose body hair. Less "furry" creatures, like Chinese people, like me, were more advanced in evolution; hence I was the superior specimen to him. To my amusement, he listened patiently to my hocus-pocus nonsense and abracadabra logic as if he thought that I sincerely believed what I was saying.

In the darkness, my lips found his eyes, and I started to fill the small wells between his eyes and nose with the softness of my lips, first on the right side, then the left. I brushed his eyelashes gently with my lips.

"Other people have eyelashes, my baby has eye . . ." I had charmed him to fill in the blank with "brushes." The game tickled me immensely, and Clyde enjoyed seeing his Hon giggle like a little girl. Later, as his memory began to fail, he could still follow me when cued.

"Other people have eyelashes, my baby has eye . . ."

"Lashes."

"No."

"Eye."

"Bru . . ."

"Brush."

I rewarded Clyde with a huge hug.

I took a last look at the baby monitor on my nightstand. Clyde was sleeping soundly, just like a baby. I could hear his peaceful snoring through the monitor. I sighed deeply. He was so close, yet so far beyond my reach.

Some time ago, somewhere, I had read about phantom limb syndrome, the sensation that an amputated arm or leg could send feelings to the brain as if it were still attached. In one of the studies on this subject, the authors stated, "This finding extends our understanding of the brain's plasticity because it is evidence that profound changes in the mental representation of the body can be induced purely by internal brain mechanism."[65] I had lost a very precious part of myself—my other half. Could my brain bring my Clyde back, however much of a phantom his former self might be?

Turning off the bedside lamp, I clasped my hands together and prayed to God Almighty without knowing to which deity I was addressing my words:

Dear God, please, bring Clyde back in my dreams tonight!

Ganesha (the elephant god) and Shakyamuni.

"...so why, when we are apart, is the moon always full?"

When will the brilliant moon appear? 明月幾時有？

I ask the azure sky, cup of wine in hand. 把酒問青天。

I do not know what year it is this evening 不知天上宮闕

within the palace gates of heaven. 今夕是何年。

I would ride there on the wind, 我欲乘風歸去，

but fear I could not bear the cold 又恐瓊樓玉宇

in those jeweled towers and jade halls aloft. 高處不勝寒。

Arising, I dance and sway in the moon-chilled
   shadows; 起舞弄清影，

How could this resemble the human realm? 何似在人間？

Twenty

THE WANING CRESCENT

Circling the red pavilion,　　　　　　轉朱閣，

falling across the damask-draped door,　低綺戶，

moonlight illumines our wakefulness.　照無眠。

No reason to resent us—　　　　　　不應有恨，

so why, when we are apart, is the moon
*   always full?*　　　　　　　　　何事長向別時圓？

People live with sorrow and joy, separation
*   and reunion;*　　　　　　　　人有悲歡離合，

The moon grows dark, then light, waxes full,
*   wanes again.*　　　　　　　　月有陰晴圓缺，

Perfection has ever been elusive.　　此事古難全。

Would that we could live forever　　但願人長久，

and share the beauty of the moon across
*   a thousand miles.*　　　　　　千里共嬋娟。

—Su Shi (蘇軾), "To the Tune of Water Melody (水调歌头)"

Tʜᴇsᴇ ᴀʀᴇ ᴛʜᴇ ʟɪɴᴇs ᴏғ ᴀ ᴘᴏᴇᴍ by Su Shi (蘇軾, 1037–1101), a distinguished Chinese poet and scholar of the Song dynasty (960–1279).[66] Su Shi is particularly remembered for this poem he wrote on the night of the Mid-Autumn Festival in ad 1076. In China, the Mid-Autumn Festival celebrates the harvest and family reunion; married women take this occasion to visit their parents. The festival is held when the moon is full on the fifteenth day of the eighth month of the lunar calendar, corresponding to late September or early October by the Gregorian calendar. Moon gazing is often part of the festivities. Upon seeing the full moon that night, Su Shi began to reminisce about his younger brother, Tzu-yu, whom he had not seen in many years, and lamented in verse his feelings about life's joy in union and grief at separation.

On March 13, 2010, we celebrated Clyde's seventy-ninth birthday along with Charlie's recovery from the stem cell transplant he had undergone a couple of months before. I served a home-cooked dinner; Ronnie made a cake; Candace, Clyde's first hospice nurse and now a close friend of ours, brought a bouquet of flowers and a balloon; and Yolanda, our Chinese caregiver at the time, came with her husband and son.

It was hard for me to imagine going through so many years without the support of all these people. Counting my blessings as smart people often do in hard times and putting things in perspective, I, the well spouse, gave my thanks to the other caregivers and I, the professor, made this remark:

"George Washington died at the age of sixty-seven, Abraham Lincoln was assassinated at fifty-six, Theodore Roosevelt died at sixty, and Franklin Roosevelt at sixty-three. Clyde has lived longer than any of these great presidents; longer than his father, who died in his sixties; and longer than the doctor predicted—he was given no more than six months after his stroke, but it has been almost two years now."

I pressed a kiss on Clyde's forehead and said to him loudly, "Baby, please don't feel depraved, because you are definitely not deprived." I was twisting the lines from *West Side Story*, which Clyde said I should know as an educated American, and we watched together many years before.

Clyde mumbled something incomprehensible. I took it as an agreement.

In the middle of reminiscing about the eventful years that had gone by, Candace said with a melancholy sigh, "Clyde won't be here for this event next year."

Ronnie replied, in his usual flamboyant manner, "You'll be surprised—next year at this time, we will all be sitting around this table again having a good time, and Clyde will still be here with us kicking and yelling."

"How can you tell?" I asked Candace, more curious than concerned. I had struggled and grieved long enough. Although I was still struggling, I was prepared to accept whatever was to come.

Candace said, "I could be wrong, but I don't think so. I have been seeing hospice patients for two decades."

"But he's eating quite well, and his grip is strong." Ronnie was not ready to accept her prognosis.

"That's why I don't think he is going to be around for long. Even with his good appetite, he is losing weight. He lost another half inch on his arm this last month."

Since Clyde was not able to stand on a scale, she had been measuring Clyde's arms and recording changes in muscle mass to see if Clyde was gaining or losing weight.

We all went silent, looking at Clyde. Of course, I had more confidence in Candace's professional assessment than in Ronnie's amateur speculation. Ronnie had been a funeral director and mortician. His expertise was in the postmortem phase, not the premortem—in what led up to the end.

After a short while, Ronnie broke the silence. "I think Clyde will still be here with us. He is a tough old horse. He has surprised us many times. He will surprise us all again."

Is Ronnie talking about Clyde, or Charlie, or both? I wondered.

I put another big chunk of cake in Clyde's mouth. He swallowed it eagerly.

Another year had passed. Another birthday approaching. Although Clyde had declined a great deal, he was still here. It was SMU's spring break, and I was on my way to Shanghai to visit my aging parents. Before leaving for China, I told Charlie that I wanted to plan a birthday party for Clyde again, to be held during my absence.

"Let's invite Fong and her husband and Candace," I told Charlie. Fong, who was the last Chinese caregiver we hired since Clyde had moved back to the big-and-beautiful house, was hardly a cook. I had shown her how to prepare meals for Clyde, which mainly included soups: noodle soup, rice soup, potato soup, sweet potato soup, carrot soup, pumpkin soup, all the same consistency, thick and sticky. Clyde was showing signs of losing the ability to swallow. He frequently choked while eating and drinking. Over time, I added a few more dishes to Fong's cooking repertoire: egg custard with minced fish, meatloaf, and meatballs, all of which required minimal effort for her to prepare and even less effort for Clyde to eat. And I taught her how to do a roast. "American cooking is *velee* easy," I assured her, imitating her accent and getting a chuckle together with her. For the birthday party, she would cook roast beef with onions, celery, potatoes, and carrots. This would require a higher level of skill for Fong to prepare, and she could show off a bit. Charlie would bring chips, dips, and hors d'oeuvres, and Ronnie would make a cake without icing, as he was on a diet, again.

Charlie called Candace. "Are you free for dinner on Clyde's birthday? JoAnn is leaving for China, but she wants us to have a party again, just like last year."

"Ask Candace if she remembers her comment from last year. I told her that Clyde would still be here." Ronnie interrupted Charlie; he never let anyone's imperfection, or his own brilliance, go unnoticed.

"By no means is Clyde kicking and yelling, as you predicted." I was not going to let Ronnie think that he was the cleverest of all.

And then I rubbed the soft black-and-white fur of Meemee and Huanhuan, and said to them, "Daddy is going to have some cake, and you babies are going to have some roast beef!"

Their little eyes were shifting from Ronnie's face to mine, quietly observing this covert scuffle, trying to figure out which side to take that was more likely to benefit them.

A few days later, on March 13, 2011, Clyde, Great Depression–era baby, Korean War Air Force captain, accomplished scholar and university administrator, beloved father, grandfather, my dear husband, and most recently, Alzheimer's patient of almost nine years, with three of them in hospice care, turned eighty years of age. While waiting at O'Hare International Airport in Chicago for my flight to Shanghai, I sent the following text message to Will, Joy, and Stuey, and to Charlie and Ronnie, who were like brothers to me:

> Clyde is eighty! There will be roast beef eaten on his behalf by Charlie, Ronnie, Candace, Fong, and Robbie (Fong's husband), and Clyde will have his cake and eat it, too. After dinner, Meemee and Huanhuan will sing a Happy Birthday duet, *woof, woof!* Love to all.

It had been a year and a half since I had moved Clyde back to the big-and-beautiful house. During this period, Clyde's emaciated skeleton-like body started to curl up into a fetal position. During the day, he sat in the big blue chair with his legs curled toward his chest. We put him in a "seat belt," tying him to the back of the chair with a belt. Still, we had to pull him up constantly in the chair because he would inevitably slip down. At night I got up and went downstairs to turn his stiff, curled-up body a few times, from the east-facing fetal position to the west-facing fetal position and back to the east-facing again. It was heart-wrenching to see someone I loved so much eaten away little by little by Alzheimer's disease.

He doesn't know it. That was my only consolation.

"Good morning, Mr. Wingfield. How do you feel today?" From my bedroom upstairs, I heard Charlie's voice, always gentle, sweet like Texas honey.

"Mr. Wingfield. You are so sleepy this morning. Did you party all night?" Ronnie never stopped being obnoxious.

Then I heard Clyde screaming.

Because of Clyde's curled-up position, in order to dress him in the morning, Ronnie had to sit him up on the bed, swing his body around, so his bottom was on the edge of the bed, and then lift him up so Charlie could pull his pants up. Then Ronnie had to lift him again to put him into the big blue chair. During the day, the caregiver had to lift him up, lower him onto the toilet, and lift him up again to clean his bottom. Clyde shrieked at every movement.

Is Clyde scared when being moved?

Ronnie did not like those legs of Clyde's curled up, so he wrestled with them, trying to straighten them out. They were stiff, stubbornly resisting any effort to unbend them. Ronnie applied more force to press them down, and Clyde cried out loudly.

Is Clyde in pain?

Since Clyde no longer could voice hunger, pain, or fear, we—and especially I, as the well spouse—had to "feel" for him. My heart couldn't bear to hear these cries, so I talked to Ronnie.

"I think pressing on his legs hurts him."

"I am helping Chuck with his physical rehabilitation these days," said Ronnie. "I believe that if we straighten Clyde's legs, he may feel a little discomfort or pain, but he will be sitting up longer, will stay stronger, and will last longer, just as with the physical rehab Chuck is doing."

"But Ronnie, Charlie has a chance to have a healthy life that will last for years or decades. That makes it worthwhile to endure hardship and pain. I am not looking to prolong Clyde's life. There is no hope for improving the quality of his life—his only prospect is more deterioration, more struggles, and more misery. For whatever time Clyde has remaining, keeping him comfortable is more important to me than keeping him around. That is what I would want for myself, and that is what I want for Clyde."

Clyde's physical rehabilitation stopped. This episode made me think about the definition of compassion. Opinions differ vastly among cultures and individuals. I thought about Ernie, who had lived three doors down from Clyde at Monticello. I had seen a chess set sitting out in his room, the game half-played, which surprised me. Ernie's loving wife, Marjorie, had insisted on playing chess with him during her daily visits to help strengthen his brain.

"Of course he can play. Sometimes he pretends he can't because he doesn't want to play with me," said Marjorie.

"No way. She's in denial," said the Monticello staff.

I knew that Ernie hadn't known where the bathroom was and where he was supposed to pee. He had frequently come to Clyde's room and peed on the floor until I mercilessly locked him out. Charlie and Ronnie, who kept in contact with Marjorie and some of the Monticello staff, told me that Ernie's three children, one of them a physician, had threatened to take their mother to court to have her declared mentally incompetent in order to stop her persistent "rehabilitation" of Ernie. Shortly after Clyde had been expelled from Monticello, Ernie suffered the same fate and was removed from Monticello too, maybe because he couldn't stop peeing in other people's rooms. Marjorie moved him to another facility, where he fell and broke his hip. Marjorie, out of her love for Ernie, I am sure, insisted on surgery and physical rehabilitation. But Ernie got an infection and died a miserable death two weeks after the surgery.

When Charlie and Ronnie told me about Ernie's death, I felt relieved for him. Each life runs its course. All people, rich or poor, black or white or red or yellow or whatever color, tall or short, fat or skinny, smart or clueless, God-fearing or godless, have been given an ending that is as inevitable as the daily sunset. And that, perhaps, is the fairest thing in this world. The more we love someone, the bigger our loss is, and the more sorrow we feel. Letting go of a spouse is often uniquely painful because, for most people, the spousal relationship is uniquely intimate. To lose a spouse is to lose one's other half. For me, true compassion is unselfish. It requires empathy, the ability to project feelings beyond oneself, to feel what the other person feels. A truly compassionate person does not seek to possess or control another person, or to prolong suffering without a clear purpose. True compassion means knowing when to let go of one's precious other half.

Due to his weight loss, Clyde's hip and knee joints protruded, creating pressure points from too much sitting or lying down, which were all he could do now. Since he had little ability to adjust his position and relieve the pressure, we caregivers diligently turned him this way and that way, left and right, up and down, but still, we were not able to stimulate enough circulation to prevent bedsores. Clyde's hips and the inside of his knees became red, then purple, and then broke out in bedsores. We put a pillow between his knees, which helped. Because his body was locked in a fetal position, it was impossible to lay him on his back. Palm-sized bedsores emerged on the sides of both his hips. Frequent turning, massaging, padding with homemade cushions and hospital-grade paddings, adjusting the firmness of the air mattress, and medicating his skin with home remedies as well as lotions and ointments from hospice all turned out to be a waste of energy. I would have tried snake oil if I could have gotten my hands on some. At my wits' end, I remembered a popular Chinese folk remedy called Yunnan Baiyao (雲南白藥), a panacea of sorts, but used particularly for healing wounds. According to Wikipedia, a man named Qu Huangzhang in Yunnan Province of China developed it in 1902. The exact formula of this white powder is a national secret of China, and the drug is one of only two Class-1 protected traditional Chinese medicines, meaning the government guards the formula. It claims to remove putrefaction, promote tissue regeneration, cure chronic skin ulcers, and reduce pain, which explains why it is as popular in China as antibiotics are in the US. The Viet Cong even carried it to stop bleeding during the Vietnam War.[67]

Yunnan Baiyao. Photo from Amazon.

Somehow, it sounded worth a try. What did we have to lose, anyway?

The miracle powder must have had its following in the US because it was readily available from Chinese grocery stores in Dallas. Using hydrogen peroxide, Charlie cleaned Clyde's wounds that had been discharging pus for months. Clyde cringed in pain. Using a matchstick, I carefully spread a tiny amount of the white powder to cover the broken bedsores on his hips, and then we covered them with gauze. I thought about adding a prayer, "Buddha bless" (菩薩保佑), the Chinese version of "God bless," but decided not to for fear of offending the deities of other religions.

We did this ritual religiously twice a day. In just two or three days, the pus stopped seeping out, and then the wounds started to shrink from the edges. It took several weeks, but the persistent bedsores that had been torturing Clyde and all of us for months eventually healed, leaving only tender red-and-purple scars on Clyde's hips.

My appreciation for my heritage increased once again. This old Chinese remedy also converted Charlie and Ronnie. Among the many claims of Yunnan Baiyao was its ability to increase platelets in the blood, exactly what Charlie needed after the stem cell transplant. His platelets had yet to climb to a normal level. Charlie started taking Yunnan Baiyao—it can be taken orally. Sadly, in his case, the miracle powder failed to produce a miracle.

Around four o'clock in the morning on August 11, 2011, I woke up to the disturbing sound of Clyde's coughing.[68] Lately, his coughing had been persistent, whether he was eating, lying down, or sitting up. I had slept for barely four hours, and it had been a restless sleep. Clyde's coughing had kept both of us awake; it pained me and worried me. On the baby monitor by my bed, I could see Clyde's body shaking violently as he coughed. I put on a nightgown and went downstairs.

I checked his diaper and replaced the wet one with a fresh one. While doing that, I also examined the bedsores on his hips and knees, making sure that the palm-sized red-and-purple scars on his hips had not broken again. They were dry, but the skin was raw, as thin as plastic wrap and as fragile as the skin of an overripe peach, ready to break at the slightest touch. I shifted his position, hoping it would relieve his coughing. It seemed to help.

In a sippy cup, I mixed water with a little thickener and held it to his lips. He sipped a little. Immediately, the cough returned with overwhelming violence. He coughed as if he were expelling his guts, struggling to breathe, his face turning red and purple from choking, and the veins on his forehead and neck visibly bulging. My heart tightened and my whole body tensed, feeling his struggle and struggling with him, helplessly watching him suffocating.

Gently patting his chest until his cough subsided for a moment, I wrapped my right arm under his neck, trying to pull his back up the pillow a little. My eyes met his imploring gaze.

Hon, let me go. Help me. I felt Clyde was pleading with me.

So much suffering. Nothing but suffering. My heart was bleeding.

Dark thoughts started tossing and churning in my criminal mind. *Do other well spouses ever think what I am thinking now? Is it OK to want someone I love so much to die?*

Fortunately or unfortunately, and paradoxically, thoughts without the means do not make things happen.

Alzheimer's disease is what doctors call an ailment of "insidious onset." By the time Alzheimer's is recognizable as a disease, it has made considerable progress. Just as there is no starting point of the disease, there is no clear end point until it ends, usually after a long and miserable period that can last over a decade. I had been saying goodbye to my Clyde for nine years, longer than the four years of the First World War, or the six years of the Second World War, or the four years of the American Civil War, or even the longer eight years of the Anti-Japanese War that my parents had fought in.[69]

But this war was so much more personal, with no possibility of winning, and with no prophecy of its ending. As Clyde's protector, guardian, and well spouse, the one who continued to be in love with him, I wanted to shield him from further sufferings, I wanted to take him away from the world of afflictions, and I wanted to end his misery. Nature, or God, did not let us choose our birth, but it is we human beings who have given away our right to choose our own destiny, the ultimate destiny of death. I wished for an enlightened world where people could be allowed, and afforded the means, to leave this world without prolonged agony and with dignity.

If that is not a definition of humanity, compassion, and love, what is?

Many years ago, on a long and tedious trip to Shanghai with a layover in Tokyo's Narita Airport, Clyde became exhausted. Having been a pilot for decades, he had been conditioned not to doze off in an airplane, and he was restless. Sleeping pills made things worse, because then he was drugged but still awake. At one point, I cocooned him in my arms and caressed his face lightly with my fingers, stroking his forehead, cheeks, chin, ears, and eyelids, trying to keep his eyes shut. Rocking him gently, I softly hummed a Chinese lullaby from my childhood:[70]

The moon is bright, the wind calm.	月兒明，風兒靜
Leaves hang over the window lattice.	樹葉兒遮窗櫺
Mama's darling, drift into dream,	娘的寶寶，睡在夢中
Sleep now, drift into dream.	睡了那個，睡在夢中
The moon is bright, the wind calm,	月兒明，風兒靜
Your cradle is rocking gently.	搖籃輕擺動
Mama's darling, close your eyes,	娘的寶寶閉上眼睛
Ah, there—a tiny smile.	微微地露了笑容

"...drift into dream."

In my arms, Clyde stopped being restless, and his muscles relaxed. He finally dozed off peacefully for more than an hour, although afterward he wouldn't admit to its having been that long.

That seemed to me to be a heavenly way to say the eternal goodbye to someone dear to me when all the pleasures of life were gone for good. In the US, people can legally ease the end for a beloved family dog with the assistance of a medical professional, but not for a beloved family member.[71]

As I returned to my bed upstairs, in my mind, I heard Prospero reciting the verse:

> ... retire me to my Milan, where
> Every third thought shall be my grave.[72]

Death was not only on the mind of Shakespeare's Prospero but also on mine. The difference between Prospero and me was that he was thinking of his own mortality, while I was thinking of someone else's: Clyde's.

I prayed to all deities and prophets: Amun-Ra, Horus, Prometheus, Zeus, Shiva, Jesus Christ, Muhammad, Krishna, Buddha, Guanyin, the Goddess of Mercy ...

Please, let my Clyde go. Let him go peacefully. Please, let him not suffer any longer.

I pulled back the curtain to see if the day was about to break. A slice of the rosy clouds glowed just above the eastern horizon, and the last part of the waning crescent was fading away.

I think I am ready.

Waning crescent.

Clyde J. Wingfield, 1931–2011.

EPILOGUE

For life and death are one, even as the river and the sea are one.

—KAHLIL GIBRAN, Lebanese American poet

ON SEPTEMBER 15, 2011, MY BELOVED HUSBAND, Clyde Joye Wingfield, passed away peacefully in our big-and-beautiful house, with his daughter, Joy, and me by his side. My nine-year journey as a well spouse had ended.

Ten days later, we held a small service to celebrate Clyde's life. Many people in this memoir who navigated the troubled waters with me to care for Clyde were at the ceremony. I selected this classical Chinese poem, *To the Tune of Die Lian Hua* (蝶恋花), by Nalan Xingde (納蘭性德, 1655–1685) from the Qing dynasty, to express my sentiments:

So piteous the moon seems:　　　　　　　辛苦最憐天上月，
A full circle keeps waning,　　　　　　　一昔如環，
Waning into a half circle, and then　　　　昔昔都成缺。
all over again, night after night.　　　　　若似月輪終皎潔，
If only you could recover likewise,　　　　不辭冰雪為君熱。
from the half to the full,
your body, cold as ice, as snow,
would be brought to life
by the warmth of mine.

Irrecoverably, you left me.　　　　　　　　無那塵緣容易絕，
The swallows twitter lovingly, as before,　　燕子依然，
on the soft valance hooks.

It does not alleviate my agony
to sing through the "Autumn Elegies."
Oh that we could be a pair of butterflies
flying amidst the spring flowers,
in the next life.[73]

軟踏簾鈎說。

唱罷秋墳愁未歇，

春叢認取雙栖蝶。

With all of us listening, Charlie sang my favorite, "I Won't Have to Worry Anymore." The tune was full of pathos yet not pessimistic, his voice sweet and melancholy. As I had wished, he changed all the first-person pronouns to the second person:

> . . .
> Soon *you'll* step on Heaven's shore
> And *you* won't have to worry anymore[74]

Afterward, Charlie and Ronnie went on to do more of what they loved to do, taking care of another elderly gentleman until he passed away about a year later. Then Charlie's cancer came back viciously, severely debilitating him mentally and physically. One day in July 2014, Ronnie called me from Dallas—I had moved away from Dallas by then—telling me that one of Charlie's sisters had taken him away from the home he and Charlie shared, without Ronnie's knowing. Tragically, Charlie died two weeks later, without his beloved Ronnie by his side. It had been four and a half years since his stem cell transplant.

After Charlie's death, Ronnie finally disclosed to me that Charlie had been HIV positive. He had had Non-Hodgkin lymphoma, also known as HIV-*related* lymphoma. Non-Hodgkin lymphoma is a more malignant type of cancer than Hodgkin lymphoma. Both cancers affect a family of white blood cells known as lymphocytes that help the body fight off infections and other diseases. As a Non-Hodgkin lymphoma patient, Charlie's immune system had been severely compromised, rendering him defenseless against all kinds of infections. His survival had depended on taking antibiotics. Charlie had made Ronnie promise to keep his HIV a secret; no one, not even Charlie's siblings, including the sisters who took him and stopped his medication, had known he was HIV positive.

Did I feel betrayed? You bet!

And I was scared. I had shared my home with Charlie, cared about him deeply, and cared for him. We had sipped from the same cup, and on occasions, I had doctored his cuts and wounds. Reflecting back, I could think of so many times when we could have exchanged bodily fluids, and I could have been infected. I immediately went for an HIV test, which was negative, allaying my fear.

Then I had the chance to think. Would I have hired Charlie if he had told me that he was HIV positive? Probably not. I would have been afraid.

What would I have done if I were Charlie, needing an income to live on but knowing disclosing my condition would likely have disqualified me for the job?

Fortunately, I didn't have to respond to this question. It is too easy for us to stand on moral high grounds when thinking hypothetically and say, "I will always be truthful." For better or worse, real life is much more complicated. Though there are many clear moral boundaries, truth and falsehood, right and wrong, black and white, and good and evil are not always easy to sort out. Undoubtedly, there are many well-meaning people who have every intention of being honest and honorable, but sadly not everyone is afforded the perfect circumstance to always be noble. I believe, therefore, that being able to accept some ethical ambiguities and tolerate each other's imperfections has made us all more human, and less dogmatic and robotic.

One afternoon in July 2016, two years after Charlie's death, our nurse friend Candace found Ronnie's lifeless body on the back porch of the house he and Charlie had called home. Ronnie had most likely died of a stroke the day before, but he had effectively stopped living after Charlie's death. He had descended into a deep depression, struggled with suicidal thoughts, and had been unable to hold down a job. I tried to help, encouraging him to stay employed, sending him money to help him get on his feet again, letting him continue to live rent-free in the house I owned, calling the police to check on him when he sent notes hinting at suicide. But I couldn't save him. He had no will to go on.

A few months after Clyde's death, my dear friend Glen's wife, Jean, passed away. Glen scattered Jean's ashes in many of the places they had lived together, the happy land. He went on to fight another major battle with his own cancer, and he won. He continues to find pleasure in his academic work at SMU, teaching and making laser beams do marvelous things. He runs every day, including in occasional marathons and through his cancer treatment, and has continued to be the kindest father and grandfather to his children and grandchildren. He remains one of my closest and most admired friends.

I lost track of Sarah, the "Other Woman," and her husband, the former SMU lacrosse coach, but I know they had passed away sometime after Clyde left Monticello. I hope their departure from this world had not been a struggle.

Clyde's children have stayed in touch with me. His grandchildren are young adults now. They will always be a part of my family.

Meemee and Huanhuan, my canine children, now eleven years old, still mischievous, remain my dearest companions. We look after each other and talk to each other constantly: I in English and Chinese, and they by wiggling and waggling, yipping and yelping, howling and growling.

Soon after Clyde's death, I retired from SMU and moved away from Dallas. The years of intensive caregiving taught me how fragile life can be. On a cosmos scale, a person's life may have little meaning or significance. Life's meaning and significance may exist only within each individual and those he or she has affected. How I live through it, my relationship with myself, and my relationships with those around and beyond are what matter to me. I have lost no time filling my days with activities that challenge my mental and physical abilities: reading, writing this book, traveling the world afar, tending my small backyard garden, enjoying my family, laughing with old friends, and making new ones. It always makes me happy to show kindness to people in need, friends or strangers, and I have received abundantly from them in return.

My well-spouse years have left many memories. When I started this journey, I faced many uncertainties. I didn't know how to win a battle knowing that the end was death, with plenty of miseries in between. I wasn't sure how to preserve my love for my husband in my heart, hope for myself, and optimism for humanity. I now understand what Maya Angelou meant by saying, "We may encounter many defeats, but we must not be defeated."[75] Every adversity can be a seed for triumph. It is true that I could not stop Clyde's Alzheimer's disease—no one could—but I could choose to have hope, hoping that I would come through the ordeal not as a damaged person, but as a better and stronger person, my faith in humanity unwavering.

The Dalai Lama tells us, "When we meet real tragedy in life, we can react in two ways—either by losing hope and falling into self-destructive habits, or by using the challenge to find our inner strength. Thanks to the teachings of Buddha, I have been able to take this second way." I don't know to which deity I may owe my gratitude, but I am grateful that I was able to take the same way the Dalai Lama has wisely chosen to take. My journey as a well spouse was a humbling experience through which I not only learned my own limits and strengths but also benefited from the wisdom, compassion, and optimism of so many others.

Leonardo da Vinci once said, "While I thought that I was learning how to live, I have been learning how to die." Yes, the well-spouse journey taught me, among other things, how to think about death. I came to see that living and dying are not separate matters. They do not form a dichotomy but a continuum, along which the beginning and ending continuously converge into one another.

As I write this book, new developments in the search for a cure for Alzheimer's disease have brought new excitements and new hope. In 2016, five years after Clyde's death, researchers reported using a comprehensive thirty-six-point therapeutic program to reverse memory loss associated with Alzheimer's disease, amnestic mild cognitive impairment (aMCI), or subjective cognitive impairment (SCI). Although the study was small, only ten subjects, and it only worked for patients with mild cognitive impairment (MCI), it was a breakthrough nonetheless because until then, Alzheimer's was a one-way slope. Every afflicted person went downhill; no one ever climbed up.[76]

In July 2018, Boston biotech company Biogen Inc. and Japan's Eisai Co. reported that their experimental drug, code-named BAN2401, slowed the progression of Alzheimer's disease compared with a placebo in study subjects taking the highest dose. The drug also reduced the clumps of beta-amyloid (aβ) that build up in the brains of patients and are thought to be the cause of memory loss.[77] Caregivers and doctors cheered at the news, and people rewarded the companies by bidding up the shares in the companies by double-digit percentages. On October 22, 2019, Biogen announced that it will pursue US Food and Drug Administration approval for the drug, aducanumab, based on new analysis of a larger dataset from phase 3 studies of the drug.[78]

George G. Glenner was a world-renowned scientist for his study of the amyloid protein. His 1984 work on beta-amyloid serves as the basis for research by molecular biologists into the cause of Alzheimer's disease. Ironically, in 1995 at the age of sixty-seven, he died of "a rare disease called systemic senile amyloidosis, in which the amyloid protein blocks the blood vessels of the heart."[79] David Shenk, in his book *The Forgetting*, records the following:

> Just before he died in 1995, Glenner was asked if he thought there would be a cure for Alzheimer's.
> "Of course," he said."[80]

Until that day comes, our pursuit to stop Alzheimer's disease will continue in full force. Meanwhile, well spouses and other caregivers, each in our own way, will continue to search for safe passages while caring for the many millions of Alzheimer's patients around the world.

To all well spouses and caregivers: may you find hope and strength within you, and I wish you well.

Life goes on …

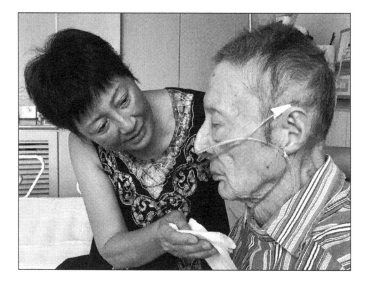

Top left: With a guide in the Yarlung Zangbo River Valley, altitude 14,042 feet, Tibet, 2017.
Top right: Meemee and Huanhuan are learning classical Chinese poems, Seattle, 2016.
Bottom: Author visiting her dad at Huadong Hospital, Shanghai, 2017.

Author with her brother and sisters, Shanghai, 2017.

Author with her mom,
ninety-four years old,
Shanghai, 2019.

ABOUT THE AUTHOR

JOANN WINGFIELD (蓝江) grew up in Shanghai, China. The Cultural Revolution (1966–1976) interrupted her schooling when she was thirteen. At sixteen, like millions of youngsters in Chinese cities, she was sent to Inner Mongolia to work in the fields. Later she went to university in Inner Mongolia and taught English in China before coming to the United States to pursue graduate studies. She earned a doctorate in instructional technology in 1993 from Northern Illinois University, where she met her future husband, Clyde Wingfield. She worked as a tenured professor and a higher education administrator in various universities until her retirement in 2011. This is her first nonacademic publication. She lives in Seattle, Washington, with her canine babies.

NOTES

[1] Alzheimer's Disease International, "Dementia Statistics," *The Global Voice on Dementia,* Alzheimer's Disease International, accessed November 2, 2019, https://www.alz.co.uk/research/statistics.

[2] Alzheimer's Association, "2019 Alzheimer's Disease Facts and Figures," accessed November 2, 2019, https://www.alz.org/media/Documents/alzheimers-facts-and-figures-2019-r.pdf, 15–38.

[3] Ibid.

[4] This quote was frequently attributed to Confucius on the internet. My exhaustive search of the original Confucius texts has failed to identify its origin.

[5] Stephen Foster, "Old Black Joe," published by Firth, Pond & Co., New York, 1860.

[6] Maya Angelou, *All God's Children Need Traveling Shoes* (New York: Vintage Books, 1991), 196.

[7] Lu Xun, "Kong Yiji," *Diary of a Madman and Other Stories,* trans. William A. Lyell (Honolulu: University of Hawai'i Press, 1990), 44.

[8] "Samuel Fuller: About Film Noir," *Images,* accessed November 9, 2019, http://www.imagesjournal.com/issue10/features/fuller/.

[9] NYC joke: "How do I get to Carnegie Hall?" "Practice, practice, and practice."

[10] David Shenk, *The Forgetting: Alzheimer's: Portrait of an Epidemic* (New York: Anchor Books, 2003), 147.

[11] Ibid., 94.

[12] Ingrid Bauer, "German Poet Heinrich Heine's 'Die Lorelei' and Translation," ThoughtCo, accessed November 2, 2019, https://www.thoughtco.com/heinrich-heine-german-author-1444575. (My exhaustive search failed to locate the translator of the English version used.)

[13] This is based on my recollection. In researching the origin of this lyric while writing this book, I found no exact match but some variations, as seen in this Appalachian tune

(North Carolina), assessed November 2, 2019, https://en.wikipedia.org/wiki/Good_Old_Mountain_Dew.

[14] "Foreign devil" was a common Chinese term referring to all foreigners. Historically, it carried a negative meaning because it was associated with foreign invasions, the Opium War, and unequal treaties China was forced to sign with foreign countries. It is still used today with or without the negative undertone. My use of the word here is facetious and endearing.

[15] Doyle Lawson & Quicksilver, "I Won't Have to Worry Anymore," original release date March 18, 2008, Crossroads Entertainment & Marketing.

[16] Shanghai cakes are inspired by baked goods introduced by Europeans who went there in the early modern era. They seem more European-style than American-style, more delicate with lighter frosting.

[17] William Blake, "Proverbs of Hell," The Marriage of Heaven and Hell, the William Blake Archive, accessed November 15, 2019, http://www.blakearchive.org/images/mhh.a.p8.100.jpg.

[18] Charlie and Ronnie said Turtle Creek Chorale was an all-gay group. I use "mostly" to be safe.

[19] William Shakespeare, *Romeo and Juliet,* act 2, scene 2, lines 47–48, in *The Oxford Shakespeare: The Complete Works of William Shakespeare,* ed. W. J. Craig (London: Oxford University Press, 1914), accessed November 15, 2019, https://www.bartleby.com/70/3822.html.

[20] "Emily Post Quotations," the Emily Post Institute, accessed November 11, 2019, https://emilypost.com/aboutemily-postquotations/.

[21] For FDR, it was "tracing the tracks," not "steps." FDR visited the hotel in 1936, by which time he had had polio for fifteen years. He was wheelchair-bound.

[22] "Why Is Pluto No Longer a Planet?," Library of Congress, accessed November 2, 2019, https://www.loc.gov/rr/scitech/mysteries/pluto.html.

[23] In Chinese classical literature, the phrase "clouds and rain" is a metaphor for sex.

[24] "Goin' Home" first appeared in Antonin Dvorak's "Largo" from the *New World Symphony* in 1922. William Arms Fisher wrote the original lyrics, which are adapted in later versions—including the one sung by Sissel Kyrkjebø.

[25] I don't remember the name of the ship. This seems to be a close guess based on my research.

[26] Martin Heidegger, *Being and Time,* trans. John Macquarrie and Edward Robinson (New York: Harper & Row, 1962), 247.

[27] Ernest Hemingway, *A Movable Feast* (New York: Bantam Books, 1964), 175.

[28] Daniel Coenn, *Mark Twain: His Words* (Amazon.com Services LLC, BookRix, 2014), Kindle.

[29] Eurythmics, "Sweet Dreams (Are Made of This)," Universal Music Publishing Group, released 1983, LP.

[30] Richard Matheson, *Somewhere in Time,* directed by Jeannot Szwarc (Los Angeles, CA: Rastar Productions, 1980.

[31] It is interesting to note that, just as Jefferson adapted ideas from French and English political and intellectual leaders, his ideas have in turn influenced others around the world, including Ho Chi Minh, an admirer of Jefferson who ironically became America's enemy during the Vietnam conflict.

[32] "To Build a Home," written by Philip France, Jason Swinscoe, and Patrick Watson, *The Cinematic Orchestra,* track 1 on *Ma Fleur,* Kobalt Music Publishing Ltd., Intrigue Music, LLC, Third Side Music Inc, October 29, 2007, compact disc.

[33] According to Wikipedia, "The Girl from Ipanema (*Garota de Ipanema*)" is a Brazilian song written in 1962 by Antônio Carlos Jobim, with Vinicius de Moraes writing Portuguese lyrics and Norman Gimbel, the English translation. It became a worldwide hit in the mid-1960s and won a Grammy for Record of the Year in 1965.

[34] Laura Hillenbrand, *Seabiscuit: An American Legend* (New York: Random House, 2001), 27–28.

[35] Sarah Josepha Hale, "Mary Had a Little Lamb" (Boston: Marsh, Capen & Lyon, May 24, 1830), accessed November 7, 2019, https://en.wikipedia.org/wiki/Mary_Had_a_Little_Lamb.

[36] William Shakespeare, *Othello, the Moor of Venice,* act 3, scene 3, lines 191–92, in *The Oxford Shakespeare: The Complete Works of William Shakespeare,* ed. W. J. Craig (London: Oxford University Press, 1914), accessed November 7, 2019, https://www.bartleby.com/70/4433.html.

[37] "Case Closed," interview with Deborah Solomon, *New York Times Sunday Magazine,* March 16, 2009, accessed November 15, 2019, https://www.nytimes.com/2009/03/22/magazine/22wwln-q4-t.html.

[38] Paula Spencer Scott, "Sex in the Nursing Home," *AARP Bulletin,* AARP, June 1, 2015, accessed November 15, 2019, http://www.aarp.org/home-family/caregiving/info-2015/sex-in-assisted-living-facilities.html.

[39] Alicia Mundy, "Of Love and Alzheimer's," *Wall Street Journal,* November 3, 2009, accessed November 15, 2019, https://www.wsj.com/articles/SB10001424052748704317704574503631569278424.

[40] Arthur Johnston and Sam Coslow wrote "Cocktails for Two," which made its debut appearance in 1934 in the film *Murder of the Vanities.* "Cocktails for Two by Duke Ellington," Songfacts, accessed November 7, 2019, https://www.songfacts.com/facts/duke-ellington/cocktails-for-two.

[41] "They Beat Their Drums," *The Book of Songs: The Ancient Chinese Classic of Poetry,* trans. Arthur Waley, ed. and trans. Joseph R. Allen (New York: Grove Press, 1996), 28.

[42] Edgar Allan Poe, "The Raven," *The Raven and Other Poems* (New York: The Berkley Publishing Group, 1990), 2–10.

[43] Nikolai Getman, *Scurvy Victims,* oil on canvas, 36.9 x 27.7", in Getman Paintings: The Soviet Gulag album, Flickr, accessed November 9, 2019, https://www.flickr.com/photos/33486233@N02/4502320357/in/album-72157623680092213/. Getman's Gulag Collection is composed of fifty paintings owned by the Victims of Communism Memorial Foundation based in Washington, DC.

[44] Aristotle, "Book II," *Nicomachean Ethics,* trans. W. D. Ross (Kitchener, Ontario: Batoche Books, 1999), 32.

[45] Richard O'Brian, "The Sword of Damocles," *The Rocky Horror Show*, directed by Jim Sharman (20th Century Fox, 1975), accessed November 5, 2019, https://www.imdb.com/title/tt0073629/.

[46] Mao Zedong, "Swimming—To the Tune of Shui Diao Ge Tou," 1956. (Mao's works have a ubiquitous presence in China, much like the Bible in many Western countries. There is no particular publisher, but children are required to be able to recite Mao's works by memorizing them.

[47] I was later told that the commonly used term for the sensation is "phantom pain."

[48] Lord Alfred Tennyson, "The Ancient Sage," *Tiresias, and Other Poems (1885)*, accessed February 9, 2020, https://www.telelib.com/authors/T/TennysonAlfred/verse/tiresias/ancientsage.html.

[49] Alzheimer's Association, "About ISTAART," accessed November 13, 2019, https://action.alz.org/personifyebusiness/Membership/ISTAART/About.aspx.

[50] According to Wikipedia, barefoot doctors (赤脚医生 chìjiǎo yīshēng) were peasants who received rudimentary medical and paramedical training during the Cultural Revolution in rural villages in China where urban-trained doctors were not present. They promoted basic hygiene, preventive health care, and family planning and treated common illnesses. The name comes from the fact that peasants often work barefoot in the rice paddies. "Barefoot doctor," accessed November 5, 2019, https://en.wikipedia.org/wiki/Barefoot_doctor.

[51] Blanche Hanalis and Laura Ingalls Wilder, *Little House on the Prairie,* season 1, episode 1, "A Harvest of Friends," directed by Michael Landon, produced by Ed Friendly Productions and National Broadcasting Company (NBC), aired on September 11, 1974, on NBC.

[52] The Gobbledok was a pale brownish alien in the TV ad for Smith's Potato Crisps in Australia from 1987 to 1994. The Gobbledok had an obsession for eating Smith's Potato Crisps, and "chippie, chippie, chippie!" became a catchphrase.

[53] William Shakespeare, *King Lear*, act 4, scene 7, lines 74–79, in *The Oxford Shakespeare: The Complete Works of William Shakespeare,* ed. W. J. Craig (London: Oxford University Press, 1914), accessed November 11, 2019, https://www.bartleby.com/70/4347.html.

[54] Fred Rose, "Roly Poly," first performed by Bob Wills and His Texas Playboys, recorded 1946, Sony/ATV Music Publishing LLC, Universal Music Publishing Group.

55 Prosper Mérimée (1803–1870) wrote his novella *Carmen* in 1845. According to the 1903 Putnam edition of *Carmen*, "No woman is beautiful, say the Spaniards, unless she combines thirty *so's*; . . . For instance, she must have three black things: eyes, lashes, and eyebrows, etc.," (New York, G. P. Putnam's Sons) page 28.

56 "Shannon" was a 1976 song written and sung by Henry Gross about the passing of a dog of the same name. From the album *Release*, Lifesong, produced by Cashwest Productions Inc., released February 1976, 7".

57 Mark Twain, "Voyage Home," *The Writings of Mark Twain*, vol. 33 (New York: Gabriel Wells, 1923), 1567.

58 G. D. Spradlin and Michael Sheen, *Apocalypse Now*, directed by Francis Ford Coppola (San Francisco/Los Angeles: American Zoetrope, 1979).

59 Nancy Mace and Peter Rabins, *The 36-Hour Day* (Baltimore: John Hopkins University Press, 1999).

60 George Saunders, *Lincoln in the Bardo* (New York: Random House, 2017), 303.

61 Cui Hu (崔护 772–846), a Tang dynasty poet, is most known for this oft-quoted and widely loved ancient Chinese poem because it captures a seemingly simple life experience familiar to so many people of every era.

62 Charlotte Bronte, *Jane Eyre* (New York: Harper & Brothers, 1850), 462.

63 Marion Deutsche Cohen, *Dirty Details: The Days and Nights of a Well Spouse* (Philadelphia: Temple University Press, 1996), 15.

64 Lisa Genova, *Still Alice* (New York: Simon & Schuster, 2009), 230.

65 G. Lorimer Moseley and P. Brugger, "Interdependence of Movement and Anatomy Persists When Amputees Learn a Physiologically Impossible Movement of Their Phantom Limb," *Proceedings of the National Academy of Sciences*, 106, no. 44 (November 2009): 18798–18802, accessed November 15, 2019, https://doi.org/10.1073/pnas.0907151106.

66 Su Shi (蘇軾 1037–1101), also known as Su Tung-P'o (蘇東坡), a Song dynasty poet, wrote this poem with the note: "In the year bingchen (1076) on mid-autumn night, I drank merrily until the sun rose, and in my drunken stupor I wrote this poem while thinking of Ziyou" (the author's younger brother).

67 "Yunnan Baiyao," Wikipedia, accessed March 27, 2019, https://en.wikipedia.org/wiki/Yunnan_Baiyao.

68 My diary on this day documented the chapter's scenes and thoughts.

69 Historians dispute some of these numbers, but that is beyond the point here.

70 I sang this old Chinese lullaby/folk song in Chinese. For readers' convenience, the lyrics are translated to English by Dr. Catherine Barnhart.

71 About half a dozen states have death with dignity laws. Texas, though, is not among those states. It is true that these laws prevent people from acting on behalf of others to "put

them to sleep," as we say of animals, but these relatively new laws are a step toward giving terminally ill patients an alternative to prolonged suffering.

[72] William Shakespeare, *The Tempest,* act 5, scene 1, lines 344–45, in T*he Oxford Shakespeare: The Complete Works of William Shakespeare,* ed. W. J. Craig (London: Oxford University Press, 1914), accessed November 15, 2019, https://www.bartleby.com/70/1151.html.

[73] Nalan Xinde, "Piteous the Moon," *Treasury of Chinese Love Poems,* trans. and ed. Xiaolong Qiu (New York: Hippocrene Books, 2003), 167.

[74] Doyle Lawson & Quicksilver, "I Won't Have to Worry Anymore."

[75] Per original interview, Marianne Schnall, *Psychology Today* (blog), posted February 17, 2009, accessed November 15, 2019, https://www.psychologytoday.com/us/blog/the-guest-room/200902/interview-maya-angelou.

[76] Dale E. Bredesen, et al., "Reversal of Cognitive Decline in Alzheimer's Disease," *Aging* 8, no. 6 (June 12, 2016): 1250–58, accessed November 15, 2019, https://doi.org/10.18632/aging.100981.

[77] Daniela Hernandez and Peter Loftus, "Drugmakers Call Experimental Alzheimer's Drug Study Positive," *Wall Street Journal,* updated July 6, 2018, accessed November 15, 2019, https://www.wsj.com/articles/drugmakers-call-experimental-alzheimers-drug-study-outcome-positive-1530897640.

[78] Biogen, "Biogen Plans Regulatory Filing for Aducanumab in Alzheimer's Disease Based on New Analysis of Larger Dataset from Phase 3 Studies," news release, October 22, 2019, accessed November 15, 2019, http://investors.biogen.com/news-releases/news-release-details/biogen-plans-regulatory-filing-aducanumab-alzheimers-disease.

[79] "Dr. George G. Glenner; UC San Diego Alzheimer's Researcher," *Los Angeles Times,* July 15, 1995, accessed November 15, 2019, http://articles.latimes.com/1995-07-15/news/mn-24218_1_uc-san-diego.

[80] David Shenk, *The Forgetting,* 146.

Reader's Group Guide

For The Well Spouse: My Journey of Love, Resilience, and Alzheimer's

BY JOANN WINGFIELD

1. **Chapter 1:** After the author has received the news of her husband's diagnosis of Alzheimer's, what went through her mind? How would you react similarly or differently?

2. **Chapter 2:** What makes a home home? What is lost when one of the partners gets sick with Alzheimer's? What are some ways for the well spouse to cope and compensate for the losses?

3. **Chapter 4:** What should one look for when hiring a caregiver? What are the specific abilities a caregiver should have when caring for a cognitively impaired person? What are the pros and cons and the adjustment the well spouse should be aware of when having a caregiver at home?

4. **Chapter 6:** Why does the author come up with the bathroom etiquette if her husband could not understand or follow it? Is there anything you would do to elevate the situation?

5. **Chapter 7:** What are the psychological and physical changes in a couple's relationship when one of them has Alzheimer's disease? How does love endure when your life partner does not know you and cannot respond, reciprocate, or recognize you? What is the difference between a loveless relationship and a sexless relationship?

6. **Chapter 8:** Why did the author push hard for activities beyond their comfort zones? Should she have done it or not, and why? What would you do in her situation?

7. **Chapter 9:** Why did the author decide to send her husband to the assisted-living facility? What were her alternatives? What are the pros and cons of each alternative? Would you have done that or not, and why?

8. **Chapter 11:** What do you think about the fact that residents in facilities may get affectionate with other residents? In your opinion, what is permittable, and what is not? What should be done about it, if anything? What will you do if your mentally impaired spouse acts intimate with another person?

9. **Chapter 11:** What do you think about Sid's action from the Wall Street Journal article—justified or not?

10. **Chapter 12:** What do you think about the author's description of Monticello—typical or atypical? What is your reaction to Monticello's decision to boot Clyde out—disappointed, sympathetic, understanding, or something else?

11. **Chapter 13:** What is your reaction to the author's approach to dealing with her husband's constipation—stunned, disgusted, disbelieving? Do you think it was OK, understand it, or feel another way? What should she have done, in your opinion?

12. **Chapter 13:** What would you do if you were in the author's situation, dealing with the sickness of her husband and facing the caregiver's illness?

13. **Chapter 14:** Why did Clyde tell the author not to inform his children about his diagnosis? What would you do if you were the well spouse in this situation?

14. **Chapter 14:** How would your interactions with your family, friends, and strangers be similar to or different from the author's? What are some dos and don'ts when it comes to the expectations of a well spouse from the others?

15. **Chapter 14:** Was it OK for the author to bring her husband to the women's room? Why or why not?

16. **Chapter 15 and chapter 16:** How do pets help with the emotional needs of a well spouse? What are the pros and cons of having a pet in the life of a well spouse?

17. **Chapter 17:** Were the author's emotional outbursts normal? How does a well spouse prevent such outbursts?

18. **Chapter 18:** Why do you think the author has imagined that her husband, who is unable to travel anymore, is with her on the trip to Hot Springs?

19. **Chapter 20:** Was the thought in the author's mind about aiding her husband's death typical? What should be done, legally, politically, societally, etc., to help people die with dignity? What would be the different views from various camps—for example, religions, cultures, the society—on this matter? How do you feel individually about this matter?

20. **Epilogue:** How would you feel having received the truth that Charlie had been battling HIV/AIDS all those years, and that he had concealed it? Would you have had guessed that? If so, what would you have done?

Made in the USA
Columbia, SC
08 August 2021